Nutritional Bioavailability
of Manganese

ACS SYMPOSIUM SERIES **354**

Nutritional Bioavailability of Manganese

Constance Kies, EDITOR
University of Nebraska

Developed from a symposium sponsored
by the Division of Agricultural and Food Chemistry
at the 192nd Meeting
of the American Chemical Society,
Anaheim, California,
September 7–12, 1986

American Chemical Society, Washington, DC 1987

Library of Congress Cataloging-in-Publication Data

Nutritional bioavailability of manganese.
  (ACS symposium series, ISSN 0097-6156; 354)

  "Developed from a symposium sponsored by the
Division of Agricultural and Food Chemistry at the
192nd Meeting of the American Chemical Society,
Anaheim, California, September 7-12, 1986."

  Includes bibliographies and indexes.

  1. Manganese—Bioavailability—Congresses.
2. Manganese in human nutrition—Congresses.

  I. Kies, Constance, 1934-   . II. American
Chemical Society. Division of Agricultural and Food
Chemistry. III. American Chemical Society. Meeting
(192nd: 1986: Anaheim, Calif.)

  [DNLM: 1. Biological availability—congresses.
2. Manganese—metabolism—congresses.
3. Nutrition—congresses. QU 130 N976 1986]

QP535.M6N88   1987   612'.3924   87-19553
ISBN 0-8412-1433-6

Sep/ae

Chem

SD

12-14-87

ay

ACS Symposium Series

M. Joan Comstock, *Series Editor*

1987 Advisory Board

Foreword

The ACS SYMPOSIUM SERIES was founded in 1974 to provide a medium for publishing symposia quickly in book form. The format of the Series parallels that of the continuing ADVANCES IN CHEMISTRY SERIES except that, in order to save time, the papers are not typeset but are reproduced as they are submitted by the authors in camera-ready form. Papers are reviewed under the supervision of the Editors with the assistance of the Series Advisory Board and are selected to maintain the integrity of the symposia; however, verbatim reproductions of previously published papers are not accepted. Both reviews and reports of research are acceptable, because symposia may embrace both types of presentation.

Contents

Preface

Manganese nutrition in plants and animals has long been a topic of practical and esoteric research interest. However, only recently has it become a hot topic among investigators whose concerns are centered directly or indirectly around the nutritional and general physiological health of humans. At the symposium on which this book is based, information presented ranged from basic theoretical biochemistry to applied nutrition based on laboratory-controlled or field human studies and on animal research models.

The chapters in this book particularly emphasize the dietary and nondietary factors that apparently influence the absorption and use of manganese and, thus, the bioavailability and bioutilization of manganese. Updated papers that were presented at the symposium are included in this volume; several other chapters that were solicited by the editor give more complete coverage of the topic. Increased knowledge of the involvement of manganese in metabolic functions of the living organism has contributed to the current excitement about manganese research. Also contributing to this excitement is the development of instrumentation that allows for greater accuracy and ease in analysis of manganese and of organic compounds containing manganese or dependent on nutritional adequacy of manganese.

This volume is meant to present current information on the bioavailability of manganese, to share enthusiasm of the participants with other investigators who have a current or possible future interest in manganese, and to alert scientists and practitioners to this field of investigation.

I would like to acknowledge the help and hard work of Donna Hahn in organizing the symposium and this book.

Constance Kies
University of Nebraska
Lincoln, NE 68583

May 7, 1987

Chapter 1

Manganese Bioavailability Overview

Constance Kies

**Department of Human Nutrition and Food Service Management,
University of Nebraska, Lincoln, NE 68583**

Manganese is recognized as an essential nutrient for
humans and animals; however, in excessive amounts
manganese is also a toxic substance. Manganese has
been defined as being a component of several enzymes
and an activator of several other enzyme systems
although other minerals such as magnesium can substitute for manganese in many but not all of these
metabolic processes. Since nutritional adequacy
of manganese is necessary for the enzyme manganese
superoxide dismutase, research dealing with this
enzyme is of current interest. Only one case of
frank manganese deficiency in the human has been
identified and publicized in the literature.
However, animal studies indicate that manganese
deficiencies affect bone, brain and reproductive
systems. Manganese absorption from the gastrointestinal tract is thought to be poor but its
absorption is thought to be at least in part
governed by its valence state. In the United
States recent research suggests that mean manganese intakes of women are considerably lower than
are the NRC Estimated Safe and Adequate Daily
Dietary Intakes while those of formula fed infants
are greater than the NRC ESADDI listings for this
age group. Depending upon manganese source and
availability of manganese from these sources,
manganese adequacy or toxicity might be a problem
for these segments of the American population.

Manganese has been found to be an essential nutrient for the human
as well as for many other living organisms; however, in excessive
amounts, it is also a toxic material (1-6). Deficiency symptoms
for manganese in several species have been created and manganese
metabolic roles have, at least in part, been defined (5,7-15). So
called "normal" manganese concentrations in blood have been established (1,10,16). Kinetics of manganese uptake and metabolism by

0097-6156/87/0354-0001$06.00/0
© 1987 American Chemical Society

tissues under conditions of manganese toxicity and deficiency have been reviewed by Keen and Lonnerdal in this volume.

Manganese Enzymes Systems

Manganese is a component of pyruvate carboxylase and mitochondrial superoxide dismutase and activates a number of enzymes including phosphatases, kinases, decarboxylases, and glycosyltransferases that are involved in the synthesis of polysaccharides and glycoproteins (12,17,18). It is associated with the synthesis of protein, DNA, and RNA with cartilege mucopolysaccharide synthesis (5,19). Since is has also been shown to be involved in amino acid transport and catabolism, this suggests that increased protein intake might increase the need for manganese in the tissues (5). Recently, investigations of factors affecting activity levels and functions of manganese superoxide dismutase have been particularly active.

Superoxide dismutases, enzymes functioning to protect cell membranes from lipid peroxidation, have been found to exist in two forms, one containing manganese and the other containing copper and zinc (20). A relationship between manganese consumption and superoxide dismutase activity has been found. Hepatic concentrations of manganese and hepatic manganese superoxide dismutase activities were higher but hepatic copper-zinc dismutase levels were lower in ethanol fed monkeys than in control monkeys (21).

When different groups of weanling rats were fed rations containing graded levels of manganese ranging from 0.2 to 29.7 mg/kg of ration, significant correlations between dietary manganese levels with heart and kidney manganese superoxide dismutase enzyme activities, liver arginase and plasma alkaline phosphatase activities and heart, kidney, liver and plasma manganese concentrations were found; however, no changes occurred in the activities of copper-containing superoxide dismutase or glutathione peroxidase in the tissue analyzed (22).

In manganese deficiency in the chicken, manganese is replaced with magnesium so that no loss of pyruvate carboxylase occurs (23). DeRosa et al. (18) verified a decrease in manganese superoxide dismutase activity in manganese deficient rats and mice. Zidenberg-Cherr et al. (17) reported that lipid peroxidation increased to a greater extent in manganese-deficient than in manganese-sufficient rats. Concurrently manganese superoxide dismutase activity increased to a much lesser extent in the deficient animals (17). Hence, mitochondrial membrane damage found in manganese deficient animals might be due to increased free radical production due to depressed manganese superoxide dismutase activity.

Manganese Deficiency Symptoms

Manganese deficiency symptoms in animals affect three systems - bone, reproductive and brain (6,24). Impaired growth, skeletal abnormalities, depressed reproductive function and ataxia in newborn appear to be similar manganese symptoms in all species studied.

The single reported case of frank manganese deficiency in humans arose unintentionally in an adult male participating in a vitamin K deficiency study (25). Inadvertently manganese was omitted from the purified diet mixture. The signs and symptoms of weight loss,

transient dermatitis, nausea, slow growth and reddening of the hair
and beard, hypocholesterolemia and depressed vitamin K depending
clotting factors did not respond to vitamin K therapy but were
corrected by the administration of manganese.

Because of the blood lowering cholesterol effects of a manganese deficiency, involvement of manganese in lipid metabolism has
been a topic of research interest as reviewed by Johnson and Kies in
this volume.

Manganese Absorption and Excretion

Manganese is only poorly absorbed from the intestinal tract; however, absorption occurs into mucosa cells throughout the small intestines (13,26). Excretion of manganese through bile and pancreatic juice is apparently more important than absorption in maintenance of manganese homeostasis although young animals seem to lack
the ability to excrete manganese. Manganese is apparently absorbed
in the +2 valence state and competes with iron and cobalt for the
same absorption sites (27). Mechanisms of manganese uptake and
retention both in experimental animals and humans are discussed in
the chapter by Keen et al. Three of the many determinants of manganese absorption and retention are: 1) developmental status; 2)
dietary constituents; and 3) membrane translocation of the element.
However, much of the information on manganese absorption has been
obtained from animal studies with the assumption made that these
mechanisms also apply to humans.

Other nutrients have been found to influence the absorption of
manganese. Manganese absorption has been found to be associated
with high intakes of dietary calcium as discussed by McDermott and
Kies in this volume. The possible relationships of calcium, manganese and bone health may be of importance in the occurrence of
osteoporosis as discussed by Strauss and Saltman in another chapter.
Since iron and manganese compete for binding sites in the intestines
it is not surprising that dietary iron apparently inhibits manganese
utilized as discussed in the chapter by Gruden.

Dietary Manganese Needs and Intakes of Humans

Because of a lack of information on manganese contents of foods,
manganese intakes are not usually included in nutrient intake
surveys. However, the several surveys which have been done in the
United States and in the United Kingdom have yielded somewhat similar
results regarding usual manganese intakes of human adult populations.
Schroeder et al. (6) estimated manganese intakes to be between 2.2
and 8.8 mg/day; Wenlock et al. (28) estimated mean intakes to be 4.6
mg/day and Waslien (29) found intakes to range from 0.9 to 7.0 mg/
day. Using analyzed, model U.S. diets, Pennington et al. (30) found
adult intakes of manganese to range from 3.52 to 3.67 mg/day during
the 1977-1982 time period. At the University of Nebraska, manganese
intakes of young college women consuming self-selected diets ranged
from 0.8 to 5.2 mg/day with a mean of 1.28 mg/day as estimated from
one week dietary diaries and from analyses of manganese contents of
feces (31).

An interesting recent paper (32) included not only analyzed
manganese contents of a large number of foods based on an excellent

sampling procedure but also included estimated mean manganese levels
of eight age-sex group diets compared with the NRC Estimated Safe
and Adequate Daily Dietary Intakes (ESADDI). The mean intake of 1.10
mg manganese/day for 6-11 month infants slightly exceeded the ESADDI
and that for the two-year old child was on the very high end of the
scale (a mean intake of 1.47 related to a ESADDI scale of 1.00-
1.50). For all of the male group, the mean manganese intakes were
within the range limits of the ESADDI's but were toward the lower end
of the scale. For all female groups, the mean manganese intakes were
considerably below the ESADDI's. Since the ESADDI's for men and
women are the same, the low intakes of manganese of women in comparison to the ESADDI's are in part due to the lower food intakes of
women due to lower caloric needs. However, these data do suggest
that manganese intakes for many Americans may be seriously low.

Manganese Content of Milk and Infant Formulas

Estimation of manganese intakes of infants has been an area of particular research intensity. While estimations of manganese content
of human milk vary, there is general agreement that the manganese
content of human milk is substantially lower than that of cow's milk
(33). Manganese in cow's milk is combined with different and smaller
protein molecules than is that of human milk (34-36). Degree of
absorption may be different depending upon ligan binding in this milk
and may be different than that of free manganese from supplemental
manganese salts.
     This has created something of a dilemma for producers of infant
formulas for bottle feeding which has led to a diversity of levels
of manganese content in these products. Since human milk, cow's
milk and/or formula are the principal foods consumed by infants,
manganese intakes are determined to a large extent by the quantita-
tive manganese contents of these substances. Breast milk-fed
infants, therefore, have lower intakes of manganese than those fed
cow's milk formulas but whether or not the manganese is equally
available is unknown. In this book, Lonnerdal et al. present evidence that manganese retention from milk and from milk formulas is
high while that from soy formulas is much lower.

Manganese Contents of Foods

Foods vary in their contents of manganese (32,37,38). Comparisons
of manganese contents of different foods are given in Table I.
Plant origin foods such as tea, whole grain cereals, some dark green
leafy vegetables, and nuts contain high amounts of manganese. However, these products often concurrently contain high amounts of
tannins, oxalates, phytates and fiber. These dietary constituents
have been found to inhibit the absorption of other minerals; hence,
might have a negative effect on manganese absorption.
     Animal origin products such as eggs, milk, fish, red meats and
poultry contain low amounts of manganese. Absorption of such
minerals as iron, copper, phosphorus and calcium is superior from
animals products than from plant-origin foods. As reported by Kies
et al. (in this book), manganese apparently is better absorbed by
humans from meals containing meat and fish than from those containing plant-protein replacement products. Because of the low content

Table I.   Comparative Manganese Contents of Foods

Food Item	mg Mn/100 g Food[1]
Milk and milk products	
Cheese, American processed	0.0464
Meat, poultry, fish, eggs	
Beef, ground, cooked	0.019
Beef, chuck, oven-roasted	0.025
Chicken, oven-roasted	0.046
Frankfurters	0.024
Fish fillet	0.058
Egg, soft boiled	0.037
Legumes and nuts	
Pork and beans, canned	0.315
Peanut butter	1.322
Grains and grain products	
Rice, white, enriched, cooked	0.807
White bread, enriched	0.376
Corn bread	0.315
Biscuits	0.244
Whole wheat bread	1.120
Fruits	
Peaches, canned	0.017
Applesauce, canned	0.014
Fruit cocktail, canned	0.122
Pears, canned	trace
Cherries, sweet	0.085
Vegetables	
Coleslaw with dressing	0.093
Cauliflower	0.102
French fries	0.150
Mashed potatoes	0.075
Boiled potatoes	0.083
Spinach, canned or frozen	0.501
Mixed dishes	
Beef-vegetable stew	0.101
Pizza, cheeze	0.259
Chili con carne	0.140
Chicken noodle casserole	0.140
Vegetable beef soup	0.181
Desserts	
Yellow cake	0.390
Pumpkin pie	0.620
Gelatin dessert	0.005

[1] These values were recalculated from those reported by Tack (50) and are in reasonably good agreement with those reported by Pennington et al. (32) and Gormican et al. (38).

of manganese in meat and fish, this implies manganese absorption and
retention from these products is excellent and implies that these
animal origin products enhance utilization of manganese supplied by
plant-origin products as well.

Methods of Evaluation of Manganese Status

Most studies on factors affecting manganese needs of human subjects
have employed the manganese balance technique during short-term
feeding periods ranging from five to 14 days. However, measurements
of other tissue, blood or urine components might be of value in
assessment of nutritional status of humans or animals. For example,
children with learning disabilities have been reported to have high
hair manganese levels (39), elevated blood serum levels of manganese have been reported in such disease states as congestive heart
failure (40), infections (40) and Alzheimer-like diseases (41) and
elevated manganese concentrations in whold blood have been found in
individuals with excess manganese intake (42,43), rheumatoid
arthritis (44) and iron-deficiency anemia (45). Whole blood manganese levels of many but not all adults with convulsive disorders
have been found to be lower than in normal controls (46).

Basis for Manganese "Safe Intake Levels"

The Food and Nutrition Board, National Research Council, National
Academy of Sciences (47) has listed safe intake levels of manganese
although information was, at the time of the 1980 listing, too
fragmentary for exact recommendations to be made. These manganese
"safe intake level" listings were as follows: 2.5-5.0 mg/day for
adults, 0.7-1.0 mg/day for infants and 1.0-5.0 mg/day for toddlers.
     In laboratory controlled studies, positive manganese balances
(calculated from the formula: manganese balance = dietary manganese
- fecal manganese - urine manganese) have been observed when subjects
were maintained at 2.5 mg manganese/day or higher but negative balances occurred when subjects were fed 0.7 mg manganese/day (48). An
extensive review of the literature relative to human studies on
manganese requirements of humans is presented by Freeland-Graves et
al. in this volume. A factorial method for estimation of manganese
requirements of humans is given by these authors.
     In recent studies reported by Rao and Rao (49), Indian men
required 3.72 mg manganese/day to maintain manganese balance. In
studies conducted at the University of Nebraska, American adult
subjects also failed to be in manganese balance when manganese intake
was maintained at 2.5 mg/day (31).
     Current estimation of dietary manganese adequacy may be too
low, particularly if diets contain substantial amounts of fiber or
are based largely on plant products. However, for meat containing
diets, the current estimated levels of adequacy may be quite adequate.

Conclusion

While manganese nutritional status is not currently recognized as a
problem in the United States or in the rest of the world, certain
groups may have less than optimal manganese nutritional status

because of lower intakes than previously suspected from self-selected diets. There is a need for establishment of manganese requirements for all age/sex groups consuming diet based on current or recommended food patterns. Furthermore, the feasability of expressing manganese contents of foods on the basis of biologically available manganese content rather than on chemical laboratory values deserves consideration.

Acknowledgments

Published as University of Nebraska Agricultural Research Division Journal Article Series No. 8062a. Supported by Nebraska Agricultural Research Division Project 91-031 and USDA, CSRS Regional Research Project W-143.

Literature Cited

1. Burch, R.E.; Williams, R.V.; Hahn, K.K.J.; Jutton, M.M. and Sullivan, J.F. J. Lab. Clin. Med. 1975, 86, 132.
2. Cotzias, G.C. Phys. Rev. 1958, 38, 503.
3. Kemmerer, A.R.; Elvehjam, C.A. and Hart, E.B. J. Biol. Chem. 1931, 92, 623.
4. Sandstead, H.H. Prog. in Food and Nutr. Sci. 1975, 1, 371.
5. Hurley, L.S. In Nutrition Review's Present Knowledge in Nutrition; 5th ed., Nutrition Foundation Inc.: Washington, DC, 1984; p. 558.
6. Schroeder, H.A.; Balassa, J.J. and Tipton, I.H. J. Chronic Dis. 1966, 19, 545.
7. Britton, A.A. and Cotzias, G.C. Amer. J. Physiol. 1966, 211, 203.
8. Everson, G.J. and Shrader, R.E. J. Nutr. 1968, 94, 89.
9. Hughes, E.R. and Cotzias, H.C. Amer. J. Physiol. 1960, 201, 1061.
10. Hughes, E.R.; Miller, S.T.; and Cotzias, G.C. Amer. J. Physiol. 1966, 211, 207.
11. Hurley, L.S. Fed. Proc. 1968, 21, 193.
12. Leach, R.M. In Trace Elements in Human Health and Disease; Academic Press: New York, 1976; p. 235.
13. Leach, R.M. and Lilburn, M.S. Wld. Rev. Nutr. Diet. 1978, 32, 123.
14. Maynard, L.S. and Cotzias, G.C. J. Biol. Chem. 1955, 214, 489.
15. Orent, E.R. and McCollum, C.V. J. Biol. Chem. 1931, 92, 651.
16. Sullivan, J.F.; Blotcky, A.J.; Jetton, M.M.; Hahn, H.K.; and Burch, R.G. J. Nutr. 1979, 109, 1432.
17. Zidenberg-Cherr, S.; Keen, C.L.; Lonnerdal, B.; and Hurley, L.S. J. Nutr. 1983, 133, 2498.
18. DeRosa, G.; Keen, C.L.; Leach, R.M.; and Hurley, L. J. Nutr. 1980, 110, 795.
19. Underwood, E.J. In Trace Elements in Human and Animal Nutrition, 4th ed., 1977, Academic Press: New York.
20. Lonnerdal, B.; Keen, C.L. and Hurley, L.S. FEBS Lett. 1979, 68, 1024.
21. Keen, C.L.; Tamura, T.; Lonnerdal, B.; Hurley, L.S. and Halsted, C.H. Am. J. Clin. Nutr. 1985, 41, 929.

22. Paynter, D.I. J. Nutr. 1979, 110, 437.
23. Scrutton, M.C.; Utter, M.F. and Mildvan, A.S. J. Biol. Chem. 1966, 247, 3480.
24. Cotzias, G.C.; and Greenbough, J.J. J. Clin. Inv. 1958, 37, 1298.
25. Doisy, E.A., Jr. In Trace Substances in Environmental Health; University of Missouri-Columbia Press: Columbia, MO, 1973; 6, 193.
26. Abrams, E.; Lassiter, J.N.; Miller, W.J.; Weathy, N.W.; Gentry, R.P. and Scarth, R.D. J. Ani. Sci. 1976, 42, 630.
27. Thomson, A.B.R.; Olatunbosun, D.; and Valberg, L.S. J. Lab. Clin. Inv. 1971, 78, 642.
28. Wenlock, R.W.; Buss, B.H. and Dixon, J. Br. J. Nutr. 1979, 41, 253.
29. Waslien, C.I. In Trace Elements in Human Health and Disease; Prasa, A.S., Ed.; Academic Press: New York, 1976, 2, 347.
30. Pennington, J.A.T.; Wilson, D.B.; Newell, R.F.; Harlan, B.F.; Johnson, R.D. and Vanderveen, J.E. J. Amer. Dietet. Assoc. 1984, 84, 77.
31. Kies, C. and Johnson, J. Food and Agriculture Conference, American Chemical Society, 1984.
32. Pennington, J.A.; Young, B.E.; Wilson, D.B. Johnson, R.D. and Vanderveen, J.E. J. Amer. Dietet. Assoc. 1986, 86, 876.
33. Stastny, D.; Vogel, R.S. and Picciano, M.F. Am. J. Clin. Nutr. 1984, 39, 872.
34. Chan, W.Y.; Bates, J.M., Jr.; and Rennert, O.M. J. Nutr. 1982, 112, 642.
35. Chan, W.Y.; Ramadam, T.Z.; Perlman, M.; McCaffree, M.A.; and Rennert, O.M. Nutr. Reports Int. 1980, 22, 939.
36. Lonnerdal, B.; Keen, C.L. and Hurley, L.S. Am. J. Clin. Nutr. 1985, 41, 580.
37. Dixon, J.; Buss, B.H. and Wenlock, R.W. Br. J. Nutr. 1979, 41, 253.
38. Gormican, A. J. Amer. Dietetic Assoc. 1970, 56, 397.
39. Collipp, P.J.; Chen, W.Y.; and Maitinsky, S. Ann. Nutr. Metab. 1983, 27, 488.
40. Hedges, B.; Griffith, G.C.; and Butt, E.M. Proc. Soc. Expt. Biol. Med. 1961, 107, 734.
41. Banta, R.G. and Markesbery, W.R. Neurology 1977, 27, 213.
42. Cotzias, G.C.; Miller, S.T.; and Edwards, J. J. Lab. Clin. Med. 1966, 67, 836.
43. Khandelwal, S.; Tandon, S.K. Ill. Environ. Res. 1981, 24, 82.
44. Cotzias, G.C.; Papavasilious, P.S.; Hughes, E.R.; Tang, L.; and Borg, D.C. J. Clin. Invest. 1968, 49, 992.
45. Mena, I.; Horiuchi, K.; Burke, K.; and Cotzias, G.C. Neurology 1969, 19, 100.
46. Papavasilou, P.S.; Kutt, H.; Miller, S.T.; Rosal, V.; Wang, Y.Y. and Aronson, R.B. Neurology 1979, 29, 1466.
47. Food and Nutrition Board. Recommended Dietary Allowances; 9th Rev. Ed.; National Academy of Sciences: Washington, DC, 1980.
48. McLeod, B.E. and Robinson, M.R. Br. J. Nutr. 1972, 27, 221.
49. Rao, C.N. and Rao, B.S.N. Nutr. Reports Int. 1982, 26, 1113.
50. Tack, K. 1984. M.S. Thesis, University of Nebraska-Lincoln.

RECEIVED July 21, 1987

Chapter 2

Manganese Uptake and Retention
Experimental Animal and Human Studies

Bo Lönnerdal[1,2], Carl L. Keen[1,3], J. G. Bell[1], and B. Sandström[4]

[1]Department of Nutrition, University of California—Davis, Davis, CA 95616
[2]Laboratory for Energy-Related Health Research, University of California—Davis, Davis, CA 95616
[3]Department of Internal Medicine, University of California—Davis, Davis, CA 95616
[4]Department of Clinical Nutrition, University of Gothenburg, Gothenburg, Sweden

Retention of dietary manganese is very high during the neonatal period. Later in life, retention decreases considerably, due to a combination of decreased uptake and increased excretion of absorbed Mn via bile. Studies on brush border membranes from suckling rat small intestine demonstrate two components involved in the uptake of Mn, one saturable with limited capacity and one non-saturable, indicating passive uptake above a certain level of Mn. Although mucosal factors strongly affect Mn absorption, dietary factors also influence its uptake. In early life, Mn absorption from human milk and cow's milk formula is high compared to soy formula. These differences are also observed at later stages in life, although the differences are less pronounced. Age, Mn intake and dietary factors affect Mn absorption and retention and need to be considered when establishing requirements.

At present our knowledge concerning the uptake and retention of Mn in humans and experimental animals is limited (1). The conventional balance technique has serious limitations for studying the absorption and retention of Mn due to the low retention of the element from any single meal and the slow turnover of the mineral in the body. There have been a few limited studies on the absorption and excretion of Mn using the radioisotope ^{54}Mn; yet the mechanisms of Mn absorption are not well understood. It is believed that absorption of Mn occurs throughout the length of the small intestine (2). The efficiency of Mn absorption is relatively low, and it is not thought to be under homeostatic control. For the adult human, it has been reported that approximately 3-4% of dietary Mn is absorbed (3). High levels of dietary calcium, phosphorus, and phytate have been shown to increase the requirements for Mn in several species, possibly by adsorption of Mn in

0097–6156/87/0354–0009$06.00/0

the intestinal tract resulting in a reduction of soluble element
which can be absorbed (4).

The neonatal period poses several potential problems with
regard to Mn nutrition. In contrast to other trace elements such
as iron, zinc and copper, Mn stores are not thought to be accrued
during fetal life (5); therefore, the infant may be dependent on an
adequate supply of Mn during early postnatal life and consequently
particularly susceptible to Mn deficiency since the concentration
of this element in milk is low. On the other hand, Mn absorption
is high during early life and therefore high dietary levels of Mn
may lead to excess retention. That infant formulas can contain
high levels of Mn was shown by Lonnerdal et al. (6) and Stastny et
al. (7). There have been reports correlating high hair Mn levels
to learning disabilities (8,9) in which the authors suggested
excessive Mn intake during early life resulting in neurological
disturbances. We have therefore found it important to assess the
bioavailability of Mn from various infant foods and the mechanisms
responsible for the uptake and retention of Mn.

Manganese Absorption at Different Ages

Several trace elements are known to be absorbed to a higher extent
in the newborn than in adult life. Preliminary studies by Mena (3)
indicated that infants, particularly premature infants, retain a
higher proportion of Mn than adults. This is in agreement with
studies in experimental animals. Using everted intestinal sacs
from rats of various ages, Kirchgessner et al. (10) showed that Mn
absorption decreased with increasing age. Whole body and tissue Mn
uptake studies by Gruden (11) also showed high retention of Mn in
artificially reared rat pups up to the age of 17 days, while these
values decrease substantially between days 17 and 21. In our
studies using suckling rats intubated with ^{54}Mn after fasting (12),
we also found a precipitous drop in Mn absorption but it occurred
between day 15 and day 16 (Fig. 1). These differences may be
explained by differences in experimental design or that, whatever
the mechanism behind the lower absorption, the artificial feeding
(cow milk) caused a delay of the change in Mn absorption. In rats
15 days of age or younger, about 80% of the Mn was retained 24 h
post-intubation, while by day 18 only about 30% was retained. In a
subsequent study, Raghib et al. (13) reported that Mn absorption
was lower at day 13 than at day 11 and that carcass values (including liver) were 17% and 30%, respectively. There are several
possible reasons for the difference in their results and ours.
First, they used a time period of 3 h post-intubation while we used
24 h retention values. It is obvious from their paper that the
stomach, the intestinal contents and the intestinal wall still
contained considerable quantities of radioisotope (and milk). The
fate of this Mn is, of course, not known, and may represent absorbable Mn that is "bioavailable." In our study, stomachs and intestinal perfusates were very low in radioactivity, demonstrating
complete passage of the diet. Second, we added the Mn in the small
intestinal wall to the carcass value, as we believe that this
represents a pool of Mn that is available to the body. The lower
values at day 13 reported by Raghib et al. (13) may be indicative

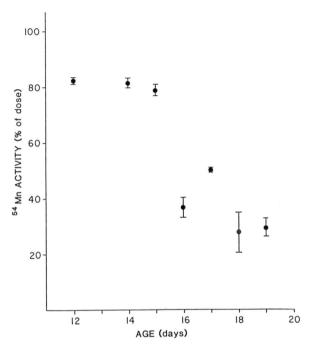

Figure 1. Whole body minus stomach, intestinal perfusate, and cecum-colon retention of ^{54}Mn in young rats 24 h postintubation (n = 2-7 per point; total n = 30; values are means $\pm$ SEM). (Reproduced with permission from Ref. 12. Copyright 1986 Lancaster Press.)

of a slower transfer of Mn across the mucosa at that age, but may
not necessarily mean that net transfer (retention) is lower. In
our studies, we found no difference in net Mn retention for day 11
and day 14 pups, although we found a higher retention in brain with
time at day 11 than at day 14, demonstrating different tissue
retention patterns at various ages (Fig. 2).

The mechanism behind the high retention of Mn at young age is
not entirely known. It has been suggested that immature biliary
function at young age may be responsible since the major pathway of
Mn excretion is via bile (14). Thus, while many trace elements are
absorbed to a high extent during neonatal life, the capacity of the
body to rid itself of potentially excessive doses of Mn has not yet
been developed. Some indirect support for this has been obtained
by balance studies on term and preterm infants (15). These authors
found a positive Mn balance that increased with the level of
dietary Mn given and they also found higher Mn retention in premature (physiologically less mature) infants. In contrast, zinc
balance was often negative, indicating that zinc, which is primarily excreted via pancreatic or mucosal secretions, could be
eliminated from the body in spite of high zinc absorption in
premature infants. Further support for the high retention of Mn in
early life is given by the study of Zlotkin and Buchanan (16) who
showed high accumulation of Mn in premature infants given total
parenteral nutrition.

Another potential explanation for the lower Mn absorption
observed after day 15 of life, is the possibility of the infant
rats starting to nibble on the solid food, from which Mn availability can be assumed to be lower than from rat milk. However, in our
study we did not see any visual signs of solid diet in the gastrointestinal tract of day 16-18 pups. In addition, we obtained
similar results when pups were separated from their dams and no
food was available for the pups post-intubation. Gruden (11) also
found these developmental changes when using artificial feeding
with cow's milk and no introduction of solid food. Therefore, it
appears that the changes are induced by changes in gastrointestinal
physiology rather than by dietary changes.

Mechanisms Behind Manganese Uptake and Retention

In order to explain the high uptake of Mn in early neonatal life,
we have studied Mn uptake by brush border membrane vesicles prepared from rats of various ages (17). This method, which is based
on the selective purification of brush border membranes and their
propensity to form vesicles in solution, allows us to study the
uptake kinetics of Mn uptake into the mucosal cell. Proper purification of the membrane can be ascertained by the use of marker
enzymes specific for the brush border membrane, functionality tests
and that the right side of the membrane is out can be assessed by
glucose uptake studies. We found that Mn uptake by such vesicles
reached a plateau earlier (i.e., was more rapid) when they were
prepared from day 14 rats than from day 18 or 21 rats. Maximum
uptake capacity was also higher (about 3-fold) at day 14 than at
the older ages studied. A possible explanation for the higher rate
and capacity for Mn uptake at younger age is a higher permeability

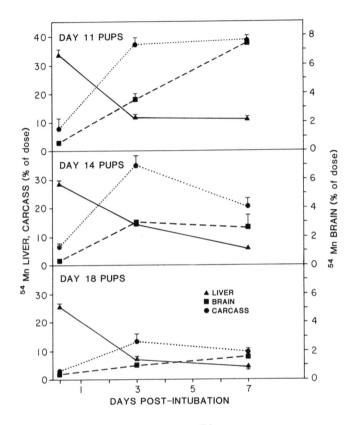

Figure 2. Uptake and retention of [54]Mn 6 h, 3 or 7 d post-intubation in rat pups intubated at ages 11, 14 or 18 d (n = 2-7 per point; total n = 41; values are means ± SEM). ▲, Liver; ●, carcass; ■, brain.

(Reproduced with permission from Ref. 12. Copyright 1986 Lancaster Press.)

of the brush border membrane at this age. Similar findings have
earlier been made for sodium (18), calcium (19), magnesium (20) and
zinc (21). Another possibility is co-transport with sodium, as all
our experiments were made in the presence of a sodium gradient.

Our results demonstrate that more than one uptake process is
operating. One appears to be a low capacity, saturable process,
which may involve a membrane receptor. The other, non-saturable
process, indicative of passive transport of the element, may occur
via diffusion and may therefore allow very high uptake of Mn. That
transport across the membrane occurred and Mn was not bound to the
membrane was demonstrated by using different osmolarities induced
by cholamine chloride. These results are in agreement with those
reported by Garcia-Aranda et al. (22) who used older rats and an
intestinal perfusion technique. They suggested that the saturable
process occurs via an active transport mechanism. We found lower
uptake of Mn in the presence of ATP and $MgCl_2$. It should be
recognized, however, that ATP can chelate Mn^{2+} and it has been
shown previously that ATP can inhibit copper and zinc uptake by
vesicle membranes (23,24). Therefore it is impossible with this
experimental design to elucidate whether this is an ATP-dependent
process or not.

A recent study in weanling rats by Weigand et al. (25) showed
that at this age, tissue Mn homeostasis can effectively be achieved
over a wide range of dietary Mn levels. A major level of control
appears to be by lowering the true absorption as expressed as
percent of Mn uptake; thus, with increasing dietary Mn, absorption
varied from 29% down to 2%. However, additional control was
exerted by increased endogenous loss of Mn (presumably via bile).
Therefore, if Mn absorption in infancy already is high and the
excretion pathway not yet developed, homeostasis may not occur.

Dietary Factors Affecting Manganese Absorption

There have been relatively few studies on Mn bioavailability from
various types of diets as well as from individual factors in the
diet. However, to better understand the requirement of Mn in
humans it is essential to obtain such information. While Mn deficiency in humans appears to be rare (see Chapter by Keen et al.),
our knowledge about the signs of human Mn deficiency as well as our
means to clinically assess Mn status is very limited. The physiological requirement of Mn, i.e., the amount that must be absorbed
to balance the daily excretion and retention in growing subjects,
is not known. The observed whole body turnover rate in human
adults (a half-life of about 40 days) and available estimates of
total body Mn content (20 mg) (26) speaks for a daily turnover of
about 0.25 mg. With a low degree of absorption, the dietary
requirement will be much higher.

Balance studies in young girls have led to an estimated
dietary requirement of 1 mg Mn/day with a suggested allowance of
1.25 mg (27). Adolescent females that were consuming ordinary
foods which were typical of their normal diets, had a negative Mn
balance at an intake of 3 mg per day (28). Other studies have
shown that in adults this daily intake leads to positive Mn
balance. While it is possible that adolescents have a higher

requirement for Mn, it was speculated that the high content of calcium in these diets may have affected Mn absorption. Balance data obtained from young women in New Zealand indicated that 2.5-3.2 mg Mn/day is required (29) and data from males in India (30) led investigators of that study to suggest a requirement of 3.7-4.1 mg/day. Guthrie and Robinson reported that a daily intake of less than 2 mg of Mn did not produce any signs of deficiency (31). A recent balance study by Friedman et al. (32) indicates a daily requirement of 2.11 mg Mn. However, as stated previously, our knowledge of the manifestations of Mn deficiency is limited.

Limited data are available about the effects of individual dietary components on absorption, and consequently the requirement, of Mn. Dietary protein and phosphorus levels (33), calcium level (34) and the effect of a partial substitution of soy protein for meat (28) have been tested in balance studies without any obvious effect of Mn absorption or retention. However, since the main route of excretion is via the bile, the conventional balance technique is probably not sensitive enough to identify dietary factors that influence Mn absorption.

In contrast to the estimated dietary requirement of approximately 35 ug/kg/day in adults, the requirement of infants has been estimated to be 0.2-0.6 ug/kg/day (35). This difference is likely explained by the differences in degree of absorption or in excretion rates and susceptibility to Mn at different ages. Because of the vulnerability of the newborn to deficiency and excess of Mn, we have investigated Mn in various infant diets and the extent to which it is absorbed. The concentration of Mn in human milk is very low, 4-8 ug/L, as compared to 20-50 ug/L in cow's milk and 50-1300 ug/L in U.S. infant formula (6,36,37). Thus, Mn intake of breast-fed infants will be 0.5-0.9 ug/kg/day, while the intake of formula-fed infants will be considerably higher and highly variable depending on the formula used.

Table 1. Manganese uptake from milks and formulas in d 14 rat pups[1]

Diet	Mn concentration	^{54}Mn retention perfused small intestine	liver	Total 24 h retention[2]	Total Mn retained
	(ug/ml)	(%)	(%)	(%)	(ng/dose fed)
Human milk	0.01	19.2±2.6	34.8±3.9	81.5	4.1
Cow milk	0.04	21.1±4.7	35.8±3.2	89.4	17.9
Cow milk formula	0.05	32.1±2.7	31.0±3.3	77.4	19.4
Soy formula	0.30	16.6±1.9	26.8±4.4	64.5	96.8

1. Adapted from Ref. 12.
2. Σ = liver, small intestine, brain, kidney, spleen, carcass.

Using our suckling rat pup model, we have found that the retention of Mn was 82% from human milk (Table 1); 89% from cow's milk; 77% from cow's milk formula and 64% from soy formula (12). Taking into account the varying levels of Mn of these diets, the amount of Mn retained per dose given was 4, 18, 19 and 97 ng, respectively, for the four different diets. If these values are

relevant to humans, infants fed cow's milk formula may retain five
times more and infants fed soy formula, 25 times more Mn than
breast-fed infants. Lower bioavailability of Mn from soy formula
as compared to human milk, cow's milk and cow's milk formula has
also been demonstrated in human adults (38). However, although a
somewhat lower absorption of Mn from soy formula, this is not
adequate to compensate for the considerably higher native Mn content of soy formula. Although it could be speculated that the
higher concentration of Mn could cause the lower percentage absorption (isotope dilution), we did not find lower absorption of Mn
when the concentration of human milk was increased to 500 times it
original concentration or when cow's milk formula Mn concentration
was increased to 100 times its original concentration (Table 2;
12).

Table 2. Effect of manganese concentration on 24-h ^{54}Mn retention
in d 15 rats [1,2,3]

Diet	Dose Mn	^{54}Mn retention			Total % retained[4]
		Small intestine	Liver	Brain	
	(mg/L)	(% of dose)			
Human milk (HM)	0.01	16.6±1.1	31.3±1.6	1.8±0.08	78.6±2.1
HM + 10 x native Mn	0.1	18.4±2.0	28.5±2.8	1.9±0.1	79.9±5.5
HM + 50 x native Mn	0.5	14.3±1.7	32.1±1.1	2.1±0.1*	85.8±1.1*
HM + 500 x native Mn	5.0	26.9±4.0*	26.9±1.7	2.1±0.2	84.5±2.2

1. Values are means ± SEM.
2. Significantly different from nonsupplemented diets by Student's
   t-test: *P ≤ 0.05.
3. Adapted from Ref. 12.
4. Σ = small intestine, liver, kidney, spleen and carcass.

Similarly, in our human studies, percent Mn retention was similar
when a 50 ug dose was given and when a 2500 ug dose was given (39).
These data are in agreement with a recent study by Weigand et al.
(25) that show substantially increased true absorption (ug) when
dietary Mn is increased. In order to assess the influence of
various components of infant diets on Mn uptake, we have identified
the compounds binding Mn in human and cow's milk (40). First, by
using ultracentrifugation and ultrafiltration, we showed that
intrinsic Mn added to milks and infant formula distributed among
major milk fractions (fat, whey, casein) in a pattern very similar
to that observed for native (cold) Mn present in these diets (Fig.
3). This strongly indicates that an extrinsic tag of Mn equili-
brates with the individual components binding Mn in these diets.
We subsequently used extrinsically labeled diets for further
fractionation by gel filtration and immunoaffinity chromatography.
Mn in human milk was found to be predominantly (about 70%) bound to
lactoferrin, the major iron-binding protein in human milk. Minor
amounts were bound to casein in human milk and the milk fat globule
membrane. It is therefore possible that changes in lactoferrin
concentration in human milk may explain the developmental pattern

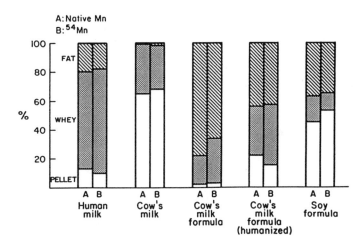

Figure 3. Distribution of extrinsic and native manganese among fractions of milks and formulas.
(Reproduced with permission from Ref. 40. Copyright 1985 American Society for Clinical Nutrition.)

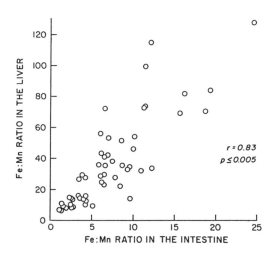

Figure 4. The relationship between iron/manganese ratio in mouse intestinal and liver.
(Reproduced with permission from Ref. 45. Copyright 1984 Raven Press.)

for Mn observed during the lactation period (36). In early lactation, lactoferrin and Mn concentrations are high and later in
lactation they both decline. Towards the end of lactation, invo-
lution of the mammary gland causes the lactoferrin concentration to
increase with a concomitant rise in Mn concentration. It should be
recognized, however, that although lactoferrin binds the major part
of Mn in human milk, the lactoferrin content of Mn as compared to
that of iron is very low (about 1:2000). In contrast to human
milk, Mn in cow's milk is mostly bound to casein (> 60%) and very
little is bound to the fat (< 2%). Similar to cow's milk, Mn in
most infant formulas is bound to casein or to insoluble material
(soy formula).

Some recent studies have assessed the effect of low molecular
weight ligands on Mn uptake. Garcia-Aranda et al. (22) found a
positive effect of histidine and citrate on Mn uptake by rat intestinal sacs. We did not find a significant effect of histidine on
Mn uptake in our brush border membrane vesicle studies (17). It is
possible that Mn uptake is so high at the younger age (which we
studied) that a pronounced effect on Mn uptake will not be observed. We found, however, a positive effect of ascorbic acid
added to the Mn solution, indicating either an effect as a reducing
agent or as a chelator, similar to what is found for iron.

The influence of iron status and dietary iron on Mn absorption
should also be recognized. An interaction between these two
elements was demonstrated already by Matrone et al. (41) who showed
impaired hemoglobin synthesis in piglets given high levels of Mn,
presumably due to decreased iron absorption. Conversely, Thomson
and Valberg (42) showed increased Mn absorption in iron-deficient
rats. We have also shown dramatically increased Mn absorption (45%
vs. 9% in controls) in an iron-deficient woman (39). In rats the
absorption and retention of Mn is relatively high for foods low in
iron such as milk. If milk is supplemented with iron, the percentage Mn absorbed is reduced (43). A significantly lower concentration of Mn in the liver has been shown in weanling mice fed iron-
supplemented milk than from those fed non-supplemented milk,
presumably reflecting lower absorption of Mn (44). Although the
functional significance of this finding remains to be determined,
the level of iron supplementation was similar to that of iron-
fortified infant formulas. Therefore, iron supplementation may
have an unwanted side effect of compromised Mn status. On the
other hand, in iron-deficient infants Mn absorption may be increased, possibly leading to excess Mn uptake. We have shown a
strong positive correlation between the ratio of Mn in intestine
and liver, indicating that the control of absorption at the mucosal
level will determine liver uptake (Figure 4) (45).

In conclusion, it is evident that further studies are needed
on Mn absorption and retention during infancy and its correlation
to dietary composition and iron status.

Literature Cited

1. Keen, C. L.; Lonnerdal, B.; Hurley, L. S. In Biochemistry of
    the Essential Ultratrace Elements; Frieden, E., Ed.; Plenum:
    New York, 1984, pp. 89-137.

2. Thomson, A. B. R.; Olatunbosun, D.; Valberg, L. S. J. Lab.
    Clin. Med. 1971, 78, 643-55.
3. Mena, I. In Disorders of Mineral Metabolism; Bronner, F. and
    Coburn, J. W., Eds.; Academic: New York, 1981; pp 233-70.
4. Davies, W. T.; Nightingale, R. Br. J. Nutr. 1975, 34, 243-58.
5. Meined, B.; Bode, J. C.; Koenig, W.; Richter, F. W. Biol.
    Neonate 1979; 36, 225-32.
6. Lonnerdal, B.; Keen, C. L.; Ohtake, M.; Tamura, T. Am. J.
    Dis. Child. 1983, 137, 433-7.
7. Stastny, D.; Vogel, R. S.; Picciano, M. F. Am. J. Clin. Nutr.
    1984, 39, 872-8.
8. Pihl, R. O.; Parkes, M. Science 1977, 198, 204-6.
9. Collipp, P. J.; Chen, S. Y.; Maitinsky, S. Ann. Nutr. Metab.
    1983, 27, 488-94.
10. Kirchgessner, M.; Schwarz, F. J.; Roth-Maier, D. A. In Trace
    Element Metabolism in Man and Animals (TEMA-4); McC. Howell,
    J., Gawthorne, J. M. and White, C. L., Eds.; Australian
    Academy of Sciences, Canberra, 1981; pp 85-8.
11. Gruden, N. Nutr. Rep. Int. 1984, 30, 553-7.
12. Keen, C. L.; Bell, J. G.; Lonnerdal, B. J. Nutr. 1986, 116,
    395-402.
13. Raghib, M. H.; Chan, W.-Y.; Rennert, O. M. Br. J. Nutr. 1986,
    55, 49-58.
14. Miller, S. T.; Cotzias, G. C.; Evert, H. A. Am. J. Physiol.
    1975, 229, 1080-4.
15. Dörner, K.; Sievers, E.; Dziadzka, S. In Human Lactation,
    Vol. 3; Goldman, A. S., Atkinson, S. A. and Hanson, L. A.,
    Eds.; Plenum: New York, 1987; (in press).
16. Zlotkin, S. H.; Buchanan, B. E. Biol. Trace Element Res.
    1986, 9, 271-9.
17. Bell, J. G.; Keen, C. L.; Lonnerdal, B. Fed. Proc. 1987; 46,
    911.
18. Ghishan, F. K.; Wilson, F. Am. J. Physiol. 1984, 248, G47-52.
19. Ghishan, F. K.; Jenkins, J. T.; Younoszai, M. K. J. Nutr.
    1980, 110, 1622-8.
20. Meneely, R. L.; Leeper, L.; Ghishan, F. K. Pediatr. Res.
    1982, 16, 295-8.
21. Ghishan, F. K.; Sobo,G. Pediatr. Res. 1983, 17, 148-51.
22. Garcia-Aranda, J. A.; Wapnir, R. A.; Lifshitz, F. J. Nutr.
    1983, 113, 2601-7.
23. Menard, M. R.; Cousins, R. J. J. Nutr. 1983, 113, 1434-42.
24. Fischer, P. W. F.; L'Abbe, M. R. Nutr. Res. 1985, 5, 759-67.
25. Weigand, E.; Kirchgessner, M.; Helbig, U. Biol. Trace Element
    Res. 1986, 10, 265-79.
26. Schroeder, H. A.; Balassa, J. J.; Tipton, I. H. J. Chron.
    Dis. 1966, 19, 545-71.
27. Engel, R. W.; Price, N. O.; Miller, R. F. J. Nutr. 1967, 92,
    197-204.
28. Greger, J. L.; Balinger, P.; Abernathy, R. P.; Bennett, O. A.;
    Peterson, T. Am. J. Clin. Nutr. 1978, 31, 117-21.
29. McLeod, B. E.; Robinson, M. F. Br. J. Nutr. 1972, 27, 221-7.
30. Rao, C. N.; Rao, B. S. N. Nutr. Rep. Int. 1982, 26, 1113-21.
31. Guthrie, B. E.; Robinson, M. F. Br. J. Nutr. 1977, 38, 55-63.

32. Friedman, B. J.; Freeland-Graves, J. H.; Bales, C. W.;
    Behmardi, F.; Shorey-Kutschke, R. L.; Willis, R. A.; Crosby,
    J. B.; Trickett, P. C.; Houston, S. D. J. Nutr. 1987, 117,
    133-43.
33. Greger, J. L.; Snedeker, S. M. J. Nutr. 1980, 110, 2243-53.
34. Spencer, H.; Asmussen, C. R.; Holtzman, R. B.; Kramer, L. Am.
    J. Clin. Nutr. 1979, 32, 1867-75.
35. Vuori, E. Br. J. Nutr. 1979, 42, 407-11.
36. Vuori, E. Acta Paediatr. Scand. 1979, 68, 571-3.
37. Lonnerdal, B.; Keen, C. L.; Hurley, L. S. Ann. Rev. Nutr.
    1981, 1, 149-74.
38. Davidsson, L.; Cederblad, A.; Lonnerdal, B.; Sandstrom, B. In
    Trace Element Metabolism in Man and Animals (TEMA-6); Hurley,
    L. S., Keen, C. L. and Lonnerdal, B., Eds.; Plenum: New York,
    1987 (in press).
39. Sandstrom, B.; Cederblad, A.; Davidsson, L.; Lonnerdal, B.
    Am. J. Clin. Nutr. 1985, 41, 842.
40. Lonnerdal, B.; Keen, C. L.; Hurley, L. S. Am. J. Clin. Nutr.
    1985, 41, 550-9.
41. Matrone, G.; Hartman, R. H.; Clawson, A. J. J. Nutr. 1959,
    67, 309-17.
42. Thomson, A. B. R.; Valberg, L. S. Am. J. Physiol. 1972, 223,
    1327-9.
43. Gruden, N. Nutr. Metab. 1977, 21, 305-9.
44. Fransson, G.-B.; Keen, C. L.; Lonnerdal, B. J. Pediatr.
    Gastroenterol. Nutr. 1983, 2, 693-700.
45. Keen, C. L.; Fransson, G.-B.; Lonnerdal, B. J. Pediatr.
    Gastroenterol. Nutr. 1984, 3, 256-61.

RECEIVED August 20, 1987

Chapter 3

Dietary Manganese Toxicity and Deficiency
Effects on Cellular Manganese Metabolism

Carl L. Keen[1,2], Sheri Zidenberg-Cherr[1,3], and Bo Lönnerdal[1,3]

[1]Department of Nutrition, University of California—Davis, Davis, CA 95616
[2]Department of Internal Medicine, University of California—Davis, Davis, CA 95616
[3]Laboratory for Energy-Related Health Research, University of California—Davis, Davis, CA 95616

The kinetics of Mn with regard to tissue uptake and metabolism under conditions of Mn toxicity and deficiency were investigated. With Mn toxicity there is a marked difference in Mn uptake among tissues. Liver, kidney and pancreas Mn uptake is higher than that by the brain, suggesting a difference in the mechanisms underlying the cellular transport of Mn into these tissues. Cellular metabolism of Mn also differs among tissues; Mn taken up by the liver under toxic conditions is initially distributed between a protein with a MW of 80,000 and low MW ligands, while in pancreatic tissue Mn is mainly associated with LMW ligands. Data on the effects of Mn deficiency on Mn uptake show that the uptake and cellular localization of the element are not influenced by a deficiency state, suggesting that the cellular uptake and binding of Mn is not amplified under deficiency conditions.

Manganese is a metal which was already recognized during the time of the ancient Roman Empire. Its name is believed to be derived from the Greek word μαγγανεια, which roughly translates as "magic" (1). Whether this derivation is or is not correct it is certainly a meaningful designation in view of the diversity of metabolic functions ascribed to this element (2) and numerous abnormalities to which either manganese deficiency or toxicity can give rise to.

The essentiality of manganese (Mn) for animals was established in 1931 by Orent and McCollum (3) and Kemmerer and co-workers (4) who demonstrated poor growth in mice and abnormal reproduction in rats fed diets deficient in the element. Today it is known that under rigidly controlled laboratory conditions, Mn deficiency results in a wide variety of structural and metabolic defects. That Mn deficiency could potentially be a problem in humans was first suggested by Doisy in 1972 (5) (Table I).

0097–6156/87/0354–0021$06.00/0
© 1987 American Chemical Society

TABLE I.   Reported Cases of Suspected Human Manganese Deficiency

Observation	Authors
Accidental Mn deficiency in a male subject	Doisy, 1972 (5)
Epileptics have low blood Mn	Papavasiliou et al., 1979 (6)
A link between mseleni disease and Mn deficiency	Fincham et al., 1981 (8)
Low tissue Mn in MSUD and PKU	Hurry and Gibson, 1982 (9)
Mn deficiency and hip dislocation in Down's syndrome	Barlow and Sylvester, 1983 (10)
Low hair Mn in infants with congenital malformations and their mothers	Saner et al., 1985 (11)
Low blood Mn in non-head injury epileptics	Carl et al., 1986 (13)
Low blood Mn in osteoporosis	Strause and Saltman, 1987 (12)
Experimental Mn deficiency in male subjects	Friedman et al., 1987 (14)

The subject described in his report was a male volunteer who
developed Mn deficiency following its accidental omission from a
purified diet that was being used to investigate the effects of
vitamin K deficiency. Signs that were associated with the feeding
of this diet that are not normally considered consequences of
vitamin K deficiency included weight loss, reddening of his black
hair, reduced growth of hair and nails, dermatitis and hypocholesterolemia. Unfortunately, it is not possible to determine with
certainty which of the above signs were actually due to Mn deficiency, since the subject was given a "control" hospital diet after
it was recognized that the element had been left out of the diet.
Thus the effects of selectively adding Mn back to this diet on the
expression of the above signs were not determined. Despite the
report of Doisy, for a considerable period of time there was little
interest in studying the role of Mn nutrition in human health, in
part due to the perception that Mn deficiency in humans would not
occur under natural conditions due to a low requirement for the
element coupled with its relatively high concentration in the diet.
      Interest in the possibility of human Mn deficiency increased
in 1979 with the report of Papavasiliou and co-workers (6) that
some epileptics were characterized by lower than normal blood
concentrations of Mn. Based on the knowledge that Mn deficiency in
experimental animals could result in increased susceptibility to
electroshock and drug-induced seizures (7), these authors suggested
that Mn deficiency could be an etiological factor for epilepsy in
some individuals.
      Subsequent to the report of Papavasiliou et al., several
investigators have hypothesized a role for abnormal Mn metabolism
in a variety of diseases. In 1981, Fincham et al. (8) suggested
that Mn deficiency may be an underlying factor in the development
of mseleni joint disease. In 1982 Hurry and Gibson (9) reported
that Mn deficiency could be a characteristic of some inborn errors
of metabolism such as maple syrup urine disease (MSUD) and phenylketonuria (PKU). Poor Mn status has also been suggested to be a

problem in adult Down's syndrome patients with secondary dislocation of the hip (10). Hip abnormalities ranged from severe epiphysitis of the femoral head to mild subluxation of the joint. The authors speculated that the hip dislocations observed in the Down's patients were related to low Mn diets fed when the subjects were infants. In 1985, Saner et al. (11) suggested that Mn deficiency may play a role as one potential factor underlying intrauterine malformations. This hypothesis was based on their observation that infants with congenital malformations, and their mothers, were characterized by low hair Mn concentrations compared to healthy infants and their mothers. Finally, Strause and Saltman (12) have obtained evidence suggesting that in some individuals Mn deficiency may be a factor in the development of osteoporosis.

Evidence for the idea that Mn deficiency may be a cause, rather than an effect, of some human pathologies has recently been provided by Carl et al. (13) who reported that the low blood Mn concentrations observed in epileptics tend to occur in the subgroup of patients characterized by epilepsy of unknown origin, rather than in the subgroup in which the epilepsy was known to be the result of head injury. This observation suggests that the low Mn concentrations are not a function of either seizure activity or medication, as these two parameters were similar in the two patient subgroups reported on. Thus, it is reasonable to suggest that Mn deficiency may be a causative factor in some epileptics.

Despite increasing recognition that Mn deficiency may be a factor underlying several human pathologies, the metabolism of this element is poorly understood. In our opinion, the recent report by Friedman and co-workers (14) concerning the relatively rapid induction of Mn deficiency in male subjects fed diets low in this element further underscores the need to understand the metabolism of this element in humans.

Manganese toxicity is also known to represent a serious health hazard to humans, with toxic intakes of the element (either through the air or diet) resulting in severe pathologies, particularly of the central nervous system (15-19). The first observation of Mn toxicity in humans was made by Couper in 1837 (15) (Table II), who reported a paralytic disease in workers of a pyrolusite (Mn dioxide) mill.

Table II. Selected Cases of Human Manganese Toxicity

Observation	Authors
Paralytic disease in workers in a pyrolusite mill	Couper, 1837 (15)
Neurological disorders due to Mn toxicity via contaminated water	Kawamura et al., 1941 (16)
Neurological disorders in Mn mine workers	Cotzias et al., 1968 (17) Mena, 1981 (18)
Mn toxicity due to excessive oral Mn supplements	Banta and Markesbury, 1977 (19)
Pancreatitis due to Mn-contaminated dialysis fluid	Taylor and Price, 1982 (20)

In 1941 Kawamura and co-workers (16) described an outbreak of Mn
toxicity in individuals who consumed water contaminated with Mn.
These individuals were characterized by neurological disorders and
a variety of soft tissue pathologies. However, Mn toxicity was not
considered as a serious health hazard until it was recognized by
Cotzias and co-workers (17) that there was a high incidence of Mn
toxicity in Mn mine workers in Chile. It has recently been estimated that the incidence of Mn toxicity in Mn mine workers in Chile
is from 1-4%, while in India the incidence is estimated to be as
high as 25% in a work force that varies between 30,000 and 100,000
individuals (18). In its more severe forms Mn toxicity can result
in a syndrome characterized by severe psychiatric symptoms, including hyperirritability, violent acts and hallucinations. The
toxicity results in a permanent crippling neurological disorder of
the extrapyramidal system, the morphological lesions of which are
similar to the lesions of Parkinson's disease (17). While the
majority of reported cases of Mn toxicity have been of individuals
exposed to excessive airborne levels of the element, in addition to
the report of Kawamura and co-workers, Banta and Markesbury (19)
have reported a case of Mn toxicity occurring in an individual who
consumed Mn supplements for several years. In addition, Taylor and
Price (20) have reported a case of pancreatitis in a patient who
received excess Mn from contaminated dialysis fluid. Given the
above evidence of pathologies associated with abnormal Mn metabolism, it is evident that we need to better understand the metabolic
handling of this element under conditions of toxicity as well as
deficiency.

Manganese Toxicity

Using the rat as a model, our research group has recently initiated
a series of investigations on the kinetics of Mn with regard to
tissue uptake and its effect on metabolism under conditions of Mn
toxicity. In our initial work (21) rats were given a single ip
injection of Mn at 2.5, 10 or 40 mg/kg BW. It was observed that
there was a rapid dose-dependent rise in tissue (plasma, liver,
brain, and kidney) Mn concentrations which was rapidly cleared.
Liver and kidney Mn uptake was much higher than that of brain,
suggesting a difference in the mechanisms underlying the cellular
transport and/or binding of Mn by these tissues (Figure 1). Gel
filtration chromatography of liver 10,000 g supernatants from rats
injected with the 10 mg/kg Mn dose showed that the majority of the
Mn was initially associated with a protein with a molecular weight
of about 80,000, and also with a low molecular weight compound (<
5,000 daltons). Suzuki and Wada (22) have suggested that this low
molecular weight fraction represents Mn that is being transferred
into the bile for excretion. We have tentatively identified the
80,000 molecular weight protein as transferrin. We suggest that
this transferrin-bound Mn may reflect a pool of Mn that will be
transported into plasma for subsequent transfer of the element to
extra-hepatic tissue.
     In addition to the effects of an acute Mn load on cellular Mn
metabolism, we observed a marked dose-dependent hyperglycemia in
the injected rats over a two hour period. This hyperglycemia

occurred with a marked drop in plasma insulin concentration (21).
The observation of hyperglycemia following Mn injection is consistent with reports that Mn can stimulate gluconeogenesis in vitro
using rat liver perfusion and liver culture systems (23-25).

An alternative explanation is that the rise in blood glucose
is the result of a Mn-induced breakdown and mobilization of liver
glycogen. To test this idea we evaluated the effects of Mn injection on blood glucose in rats that were fed, or fasted for 24 or 48
hours (26). It was found that fasting attenuated the rise in blood
glucose; thus, part of the hyperglycemic response of the Mn appears
to be due to a mobilization of liver glycogen. However, an increase in blood glucose was observed even in the 48 hour fasted
rats (180 mg/dl in Mn-injected rats versus 120 mg/dl in controls),
suggesting that processes other than glycogen breakdown were
contributing to the rise in blood glucose. For this reason we
tested the idea that the hyperglycemia may partly be due to an
effect of Mn on pancreatic function. As is shown in Figure 2,
pancreatic Mn concentrations rapidly increased following Mn injection. This increase in pancreatic Mn content was followed by a
drop in plasma insulin concentrations and a rise in plasma glucose
concentrations. These observations suggest that changes in
pancreatic Mn concentration may regulate insulin production.
Consistent with this idea are the reports of Dean and Matthews (27)
that 2.5 mM Mn can block glucose-induced action potentials in the
pancreatic B-cell; of Hermansen and Iverson (28) that 50 mM Mn can
inhibit insulin release in the isolated perfused canine pancreas;
and of Rorsman et al. (29) that in vitro, glucose can stimulate
pancreatic Mn uptake. To further test the hypothesis that changes
in pancreatic Mn concentration may be regulatory with regard to
insulin output, we studied the effects of adrenalectomy on the
Mn-induced hyperglycemia (30). This study was based on the idea
that the adrenalectomy would prevent the hyperglycemic response due
to a block in catecholamine-induced glucagon release and glycogen
breakdown. Thus we reasoned that the glucose-induced rise in
pancreatic Mn concentration should also be attenuated in these
animals. Consistent with this hypothesis, adrenalectomy blunted
Mn-induced rises in blood glucose and pancreatic Mn concentration
(Figure 3). In contrast to the pancreas, adrenalectomy had no
effect on hepatic uptake of Mn following injection. Consistent
with our results, Hughes et al. (31) have reported that long-term
adrenalectomy of normoglycemic rats does not affect hepatic Mn
concentrations. Thus the initial uptake of Mn by the pancreas may
in part be a homeostatic response of the pancreas to the hyperglycemic condition. An interesting speculation is that under
conditions of Mn toxicity, pancreatic Mn uptake is excessive and
results in a subsequent inhibition of insulin release. It should
be recognized that insulin in turn may affect the metabolism of Mn,
as hepatic and kidney concentrations of the element are markedly
increased in diabetic animals (32). While this increase in tissue
Mn concentration may be secondary to increased gluconeogenesis and
ureagenesis in the diabetic animal, a direct effect of insulin on
tissue Mn uptake and/or release has not been ruled out (32).

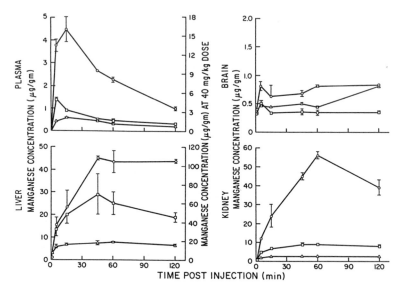

Figure 1.   Changes in tissue Mn concentrations following
injection with 2.5 (△), 10 (□) or 40 (○) mg Mn/kg BW in
Sprague-Dawley rats.
(Reproduced with permission from Ref. 21. Copyright 1984 Humana
Press.)

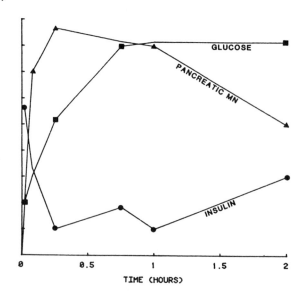

Figure 2.   Changes in pancreatic Mn (▲) plasma insulin (●) and
glucose (■) concentrations following injection of 40 mg Mn/kq
BW in Sprague-Dawley rats.
(Reproduced with permission from Ref. 26. Copyright 1985 Elsevier.)

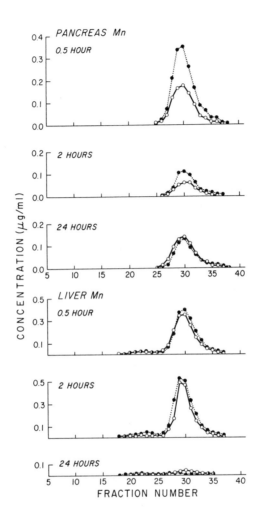

Figure 3. Changes in the molecular localization of Mn in rat liver and pancreas following injection with 10 mg Mn/kg BW. Control rats (●--●), adrenalectomized rats (○—○). Chromatography on NaBH$_4$-treated Sepharose CL-6B. Column size 1.6 x 90 cm. Buffer 0.01 ammonium acetate, pH 6.5.
(Reproduced with permission from Ref. 30. Copyright 1986 Academic Press.)

Manganese Deficiency

It is important to point out that similar to Mn toxicity, Mn deficiency can affect carbohydrate metabolism. Manganese defi- ciency has been shown to result in reduced pancreatic Mn content and insulin synthesis and release in rats and guinea pigs (33-35). When Mn-deficient animals are given a glucose load, a diabetic-type of glucose tolerance curve is observed (33,34). Thus, similar to what is observed for Mn toxicity, Mn deficiency has a profound effect on pancreatic function, strongly supporting the hypothesis that changes in intracellular Mn concentrations may be an important mechanism of cellular metabolic control in the pancreatic cell.

For the above reasons, our research group has begun to inves- tigate Mn uptake and tissue distribution under conditions of dietary adequacy and deficiency. In these studies we used both the Sprague-Dawley and Wistar strains of rat. These two strains were chosen because we have found that the Wistar rat is less sensitive to dietary Mn deficiency than is the Sprague-Dawley strain (36,37). For example, neonatal mortality in the offspring of Sprague-Dawley dams fed Mn-deficient diets during pregnancy and lactation was approximately 73%, while in the offspring of Wistar dams fed deficient diets for similar periods of time it was 30%. Similarly, the incidence of congenital ataxia, an expression of prenatal Mn deficiency (38), is over 80% in the surviving offspring of Mn- deficient Sprague-Dawley dams, while ataxia is not observed in the offspring of Wistar dams fed the deficient diet. A differential response to Mn deficiency between the strains can also be observed when control weanling rats are fed Mn-deficient diets for a period of six weeks. Sprague-Dawley rats fed the deficient diet for this period of time are characterized by lower than normal liver choles- terol concentrations (2.43 vs 2.09 mg/g for control and deficient rats, respectively), while cholesterol concentrations are normal in the Wistar rats fed the deficient diet (2.45 vs 2.48 mg/g) (37).

One interpretation of the above results is that the Wistar rat has a better ability to adapt to a Mn-deficient diet than does the Sprague-Dawley. Thus we hypothesized that this differential response to Mn deficiency between the strains would allow us to better identify metabolic responses to the consumption of Mn- deficient diets. In our initial study, weanling Sprague-Dawley and Wistar rats were fed diets containing either 45 or 1 ug Mn/g for 6 weeks. After this period, the rats were fasted overnight and then intubated with 1 g of the 1 ug Mn/g diet which was labeled with ^{54}Mn. The diet was given as a 50% slurry made with deionized water. Six hours after intubation the animals were killed and tissues were collected and counted.

Mean Mn concentrations were similar in Sprague-Dawley and Wistar rats fed the control diet (2.3 and 2.2 ug Mn/g wet weight, respectively). Manganese concentrations were markedly lower in the rats fed the deficient diets compared to the controls. Liver Mn concentrations were slightly lower in the deficient Sprague-Dawley rats than in the deficient Wistar rats (0.4 and 0.7 ug/g, respec- tively).

By 6 hours post-intubation the majority of the activity was recovered in the intestine and cecum (Figure 4). The only internal

organ which retained a substantial amount of activity at this time
was the liver. Despite the marked difference in liver Mn concentration between the deficient and control rats, there was no
difference in the amount of activity recovered in this tissue among
the different groups (Figure 5). Similarly, the subcellular
distribution of ^{54}Mn in the tissues was not affected by diet or
strain (Figure 6).

In this study the low count rate observed in extrahepatic
tissue made it difficult to characterize the effect of dietary
treatment on extrahepatic tissue Mn uptake. Therefore, a second
study was conducted in which Sprague-Dawley rats which had been fed
the control or deficient diet for 6 weeks were injected ip with
^{54}Mn and then killed four hours later. As is shown in Figure 7,
significant uptake of the isotope occurred in pancreas, kidney,
liver, heart and diaphragm in decreasing order. There were no
differences in organ distribution of the element between the deficient and control animals. Similar to the tissue distribution
data, the subcellular distribution of the isotope was unaffected by
dietary treatment. It is interesting to note that this statement
is true even in tissues such as liver and pancreas which show a
considerable difference in subcellular distribution of the element
(Figure 8). Data obtained for the Wistar rat were similar to those
obtained for the Sprague-Dawley rat.

In addition to similar tissue and subcellular distribution of
the isotope between deficient and control rats, we have obtained
preliminary evidence that 4 hours after ip injection of ^{54}Mn, the
molecular localization of the isotope in the 10,000 g liver super-
natant fraction is identical in two groups. Chromatograms for both
control and deficient rats show that a large proportion of the
isotope is recovered in the low molecular weight region, with a
sharp peak of activity occurring in the 4-6000 molecular weight
range, while a second peak of activity is associated with high
molecular weight proteins (39).

Taken together, the above data suggest that Mn deficiency does
not result in an increase in Mn absorption or an amplification of
cellular Mn uptake processes. To further test this idea, we have
investigated ^{54}Mn uptake using liver, heart and pancreas tissue
slices obtained from Mn-deficient and control rats. Tissues were
collected from rats which had been fed either control or Mn-
deficient diets for 6 weeks after weaning. Incubations were done
as described by Brandt and Schramm (40). Although liver Mn concentrations were markedly lower in the deficient rats compared to
controls, liver slice uptake of ^{54}Mn was similar in the two groups.
Similarly, despite markedly lower heart and pancreas Mn concentrations in slices from the deficient animals compared to controls,
heart and pancreatic slice uptake kinetics were similar in the two
groups (39).

Overall, these data support the idea that cellular uptake of
Mn is not a component in the regulation of cellular Mn concentrations. Thus there appears to be a poor homeostatic response of the
rat to Mn deficiency with regard to intestinal, hepatic or extra-
hepatic cellular uptake of the element. An inability to compensate
for a low dietary intake of Mn, or low tissue concentrations of Mn,
by increased cellular uptake of the element, is consistent with the

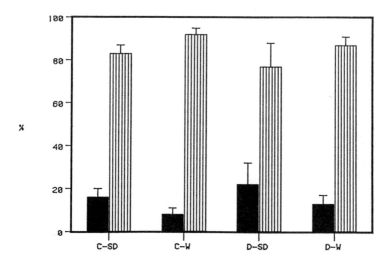

Figure 4. ^{54}Mn distribution in intestine (■) and colon (▥) 6 hours after intubation of a ^{54}Mn-labeled meal in control (C) and Mn-deficient (D) Sprague-Dawley (SD) and Wistar (W) rats.

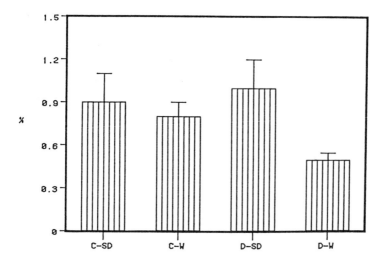

Figure 5. Liver retention of ^{54}Mn 6 hours after intubation of a ^{54}Mn-labeled meal in control (C) and Mn-deficient (D) Sprague-Dawley (SD) and Wistar (W) rats.

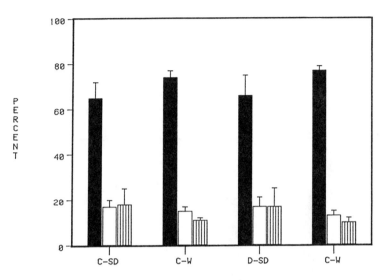

Figure 6. Nuclear (■), mitochondrial (☐) and cytosolic (▥) distribution of [54]Mn 6 hours after intubation of a [54]Mn-labeled meal in control (C) and Mn-deficient (D) Sprague-Dawley (SD) and Wistar (W) rats.

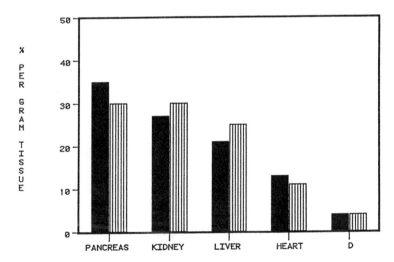

Figure 7. [54]Mn distribution in pancreas, kidney, liver, heart and diaphragm 4 hours after ip injection with [54]Mn in control (■) and Mn-deficient (▥) Sprague-Dawley rats.

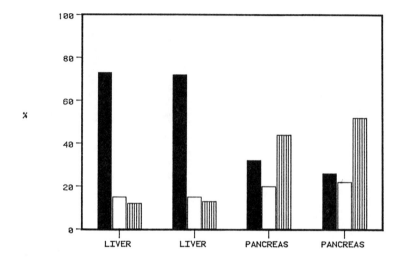

Figure 8. Liver and pancreas nuclear (■), mitochondrial (□) and cytosolic (▥) distribution of ^{54}Mn 4 hours after ip injection with ^{54}Mn in control (left) and Mn-deficient (right) Sprague-Dawley rats.

observation of recent investigators that Mn deficiency may be an underlying factor in several disease states.

Literature Cited

1. Cotzias, G. C. Physiol. Rev. 1958, 38, 503-32.
2. Keen, C. L.; Lonnerdal, B.; Hurley, L. S. In Biochemistry of the Essential Ultratrace Elements; Frieden, E., Ed.; Plenum: New York, 1984; pp 89-132.
3. Orent, E. R.; McCollum, E. V. J. Biol. Chem. 1931, 92, 651-78.
4. Kemmerer, A. R.; Elvehjem, C. A.; Hart, E. B. J. Biol. Chem. 1931, 92, 623-30.
5. Doisy, E., Jr. In Trace Substances in Environmental Health; Hemphill, D., Ed.; University of Missouri, Columbia, 1972; Vol. VI, pp 193-9.
6. Papavasiliou, P. S.; Kutt, H.; Miller, S. T.; Rosal, V.; Wang, Y. Y.; Aronson, R. B. Neurology 1979, 29, 1466-73.
7. Hurley, L. S., Woolley, D. E.; Rosenthal, F.; Timiras, P. S. Am. J. Physiol. 1963, 204, 493-6.
8. Fincham, J. E.; ven Rensburg, S. J.; Marasas, W. F. O. SA Med. J. 1981, 60, 445-7.
9. Hurry, V. J.; Gibson, R. S. Biol. Trace Element Res. 1982, 4, 157-74.
10. Barlow, P. J.; Sylvester, P. E. Lancet 1983, i, 685.
11. Saner, G.; Dagoglu, T.; Ozden, T. Am. J. Clin. Nutr. 1985, 41, 1042-4.
12. Strause, L.; Saltman, P. In Nutritional Bioavailability of Manganese; Kies, C., Ed.; American Chemical Society, Washington, DC, 1987; this volume.
13. Carl, G. F.; Keen, C. L.; Gallagher, B. B.; Clegg, M. S.; Hurley, L. S. Neurology 1986, 36, 1584-7.
14. Friedman, B. J.; Freeland-Graves, J. H.; Bales, C. W.; Behmardi, F.; Shorey-Kutschke, R. L.; Willis, R. A.; Crosby, J. B.; Trickett, P. C.; Houston, S. D. J. Nutr. 1987, 117, 133-43.
15. Couper, J. Brit. Ann. Med. Pharm. Vit. Stat. Gen. Sci. 1837, 1, 41-2.
16. Kawamura, R.; Ikuta, H.; Fukuzumi, S.; Ymada, R.; Tsubaki, S.; Kodama, T.; Kurata, S. Kisasato Arch. Exp. Med. 1941, 18, 145-69.
17. Cotzias, G. C.; Horiuchi, K.; Fuenzalida, S.; Mena, I. Neurology 1968, 18, 376-82.
18. Mena, I. In Disorders of Mineral Metabolism; Bronner, F. and Coburn, J. W., Eds.; Academic: New York, 1981; Vol. 1, pp 233-70.
19. Banta, R. G.; Markesbury, W. R. Neurology 1977, 27, 213-16.
20. Taylor, P. A.; Price, J. D. E. Canad. Med. Assoc. J. 1982, 126, 503-5.
21. Keen, C. L.; Baly, D. L.; Lonnerdal, B. Biol. Trace Element Res. 1984, 6, 309-15.
22. Suzuki, H.; Wada, O. Environ. Res. 1981, 26, 521-8.
23. Mangnall, D.; Gidding, A. E. B.; Clark, R. G. Int. J. Biochem. 1976, 7, 293-9.

24. Rognstad, R. J. Biol. Chem. 1981, 256, 1608-10.
25. Rognstad, R. In Manganese in Metabolism and Enzyme Function; Schramm, V. L. and Wedler, F. C., Eds.; Academic: New York, 1986; pp 133-45.
26. Baly, D. L.; Lonnerdal, B.; Keen, C. L. Toxicol. Lett. 1985, 25, 95-102.
27. Dean, P. M.; Matthews, E. K. J. Physiol. 1970, 210, 265-75.
28. Hermansen, K.; Iversen, J. Diabetologia 1978, 15, 475-9.
29. Rorsman, P.; Hellman, B. Biochem. J. 1983, 210, 307-14.
30. Keen, C. L.; Lonnerdal, B. In Manganese in Metabolism and Enzyme Function; Schramm, V. L. and Wedler, F. C., Eds.; Academic: Orlando, FL, 1986; pp 35-50.
31. Hughes, E. R.; Miller, S. T.; Cotzias, G. C. Am. J. Physiol. 1966, 211, 207-10.
32. Failla, M. L. In Manganese in Metabolism and Enzyme Function; Schramm, V. L. and Wedler, F. C., Eds.; Academic: New York, 1986; pp 93-105.
33. Everson, G. J.; Shrader, R. E. J. Nutr. 1968, 94, 89-94.
34. Baly, D. L.; Curry, D. L.; Keen, C. L.; Hurley, L. S. J. Nutr. 1984, 114, 1438-66.
35. Baly, D. L.; Curry, D. L.; Keen, C. L.; Hurley, L. S. Endocrinology 1985, 116, 1734-40.
36. Dungan, D. D.; Zidenberg-Cherr, S.; Keen, C. L.; Lonnerdal, B.; Hurley, L. S. Fed. Proc. 1984, 43, 1054.
37. Kawano, J.; Ney, D. N.; Keen, C. L.; Schneeman, B. O. J. Nutr. 1987, in press.
38. Hurley, L. S. Physiol. Rev. 1981, 61, 249-95.
39. Keen, C. L.; Zidenberg-Cherr, S.; Lonnerdal, B. Fed. Proc. 1987, 46, 569.
40. Brandt, M.; Schramm, V. L. In Manganese in Metabolism and Enzyme Function; Schramm, V. L. and Wedler, F. C., Eds.; Academic: New York, 1986; pp 3-16.

RECEIVED August 20, 1987

Chapter 4

Manganese Homeostasis in the Chick

L. Lee Southern[1], David H. Baker[2], and Kevin M. Halpin[2,3]

[1]Department of Animal Science, Louisiana Agricultural Experiment Station, Louisiana State University Agricultural Center, Baton Rouge, LA 70803
[2]Department of Animal Sciences, University of Illinois, Urbana, IL 61801

Manganese is a nutritionally important trace element for chicks. Dietary energy and protein sources contain very little bioavailable Mn, and these feed ingredients reduce the biopotency of inorganic Mn supplements. This adverse effect is exerted primarily in the intestine as a result of reduced Mn absorption and is mediated by the fiber and/or ash components of the feedstuffs. Gut absorption efficiencies are higher when a phytate- and fiber-free casein-dextrose diet is fed than when a corn-soybean meal diet is fed. Dietary interrelationships exist between Mn and Co and between Mn and Fe. Cobalt increases Mn absorption and may precipitate Mn toxicosis. Excess dietary Mn reduces Fe utilization, but excess Fe does not affect Mn utilization. Eimeria acervulina infection increases Mn absorption.

Manganese nutriture of the chick has been a fertile area of investigation for over 50 years. Wilgus and associates (1) in 1936 reported that Mn would prevent perosis in chicks. Numerous research publications have since expanded the knowledge of Mn homeostasis in the chick. The chick is unique with regard to Mn. It has a higher Mn requirement than it's mammalian counterpart, and the Mn absorption efficiency in chicks is thought to be less than in mammals (2).
  The purpose of this report will be to review current aspects of Mn homeostasis in the chick. In particular, Mn absorption

[3]Current address: National Dairy Council, 6300 North River Road, Rosemont, IL 60018

efficiency, storage, turnover, interactions with other microminerals and with macrominerals, effect of coccidial infections,
requirement and toxicity, and bioavailability of Mn in conventional poultry feeds and in inorganic Mn supplements will be
addressed.

Bioavailability: Feedstuffs and Inorganic Supplements

Conventional Poultry Feedstuffs. Manganese is one of only two
or three trace elements that must be supplemented to conventional poultry diets. This requirement for supplementation necessi-
tates knowledge of Mn bioavailability in poultry feedstuffs.
Davis and coworkers (3) reported that soybean protein reduced Mn
utilization, Holmes and Roberts (4) observed an increased incidence of perosis in chicks fed rapeseed meal and Seth and Clandinin (5) reported that rapeseed meal not only increased the incidence of perosis, but that it reduced the perosis-preventative
efficacy of inorganic Mn supplements. More recently, Halpin and
Baker (6) concluded that corn, soybean meal, fish meal, wheat
bran and rice bran reduced Mn deposition in bone, bile and pancreas (Mn responsive tissues) when added to a casein-dextrose
diet containing 1000 ppm Mn. With the exception of rice bran,
these feed ingredients also reduced tissue Mn concentrations
when the dietary supplemental level of Mn was reduced to 14 ppm
(the Mn requirement of chicks consuming casein-dextrose diets).
Rice bran provided bioavailable Mn when the diet was at or below
the chick's Mn requirement. These experiments were conducted
for two-week periods and, although supplementation of these feed
ingredients to the casein-dextrose diet appeared to reduce Mn
availability, chick gain and efficiency of gain were not adversely affected. In a subsequent seven-week investigation (7),
fish meal, wheat bran and a corn-soybean meal mixture (57% corn
and 43% soybean meal to simulate ingredient ratios in a 23%
crude protein diet) reduced chick performance and tissue Mn concentration when added to the casein-dextrose diet containing 14
ppm Mn. Only fish meal had a detrimental effect when added to a
Mn-deficient diet (7 ppm Mn). Fish meal reduced gain, feed
efficiency and tissue Mn concentrations, and it also increased
the incidence and severity of perosis. Wheat bran and the corn-
soybean meal mixture, however, increased bone Mn concentration
when added to the diet containing 7 ppm Mn. These researchers
concluded from the long-term investigation that wheat bran and
the corn-soybean meal mixture provided bioavailable Mn when the
chick was threatened with a Mn deficit, but not when the diet
contained adequate (or marginally adequate) Mn. Fish meal, on
the other hand, contained no bioavailable Mn, regardless of Mn
concentration in the diet. Thompson and Weber (8) conducted a
similar investigation over a four-week period using a soybean
meal-dextrose basal diet. They added cellulose (6%), wheat bran
(12%), corn bran (9.7%), soy bran (9.7%), oat hulls (7.3%) and
rice bran (16.67%) to the basal diet such that feed ingredient
additions supplied approximately 6% dietary neutral detergent
fiber (NDF). These researchers concluded that rice bran reduced

growth, feed efficiency and bone Mn concentration compared with the basal diet. The other "fiber" sources did not adversely affect chick performance or bone and liver Mn deposition. These results differ slightly from those of Halpin and Baker (6-7), but investigational dissimilarities such as fiber content and Mn level in the basal diets probably account for the discrepancies. Halpin and Baker's diet contained known amounts of inorganic Mn and was essentially devoid of fiber. Thompson and Weber's basal diet, however, contained 3.8% neutral detergent fiber from soybean meal and 117 ppm Mn from a mixture of both organic and inorganic sources.

Although minor differences are evident in the research describing Mn bioavailability, it is clear that most conventional poultry feedstuffs contain very little bioavailable Mn, and in many cases, they actually reduce availability of inorganic Mn supplements.

The mechanism by which this reduction in availability occurs was recently evaluated (9). Chicks were fed 2000 ppm Mn for 14 days and then placed on diets containing 14 ppm Mn with or without 10% wheat bran supplementation. Chicks were killed serially for two weeks following the period of Mn "loading". Tissue Mn levels decreased with time, but wheat bran did not affect rate of tissue Mn depletion. Thus, wheat bran did not affect homeostasis of stored Mn. In another experiment (9), 10% dietary wheat bran was fed to chicks receiving varying amounts of inorganic Mn administered via intraperitoneal injection. Wheat bran erratically altered tissue Mn concentrations, but its effect did not approach the magnitude and consistency of that occurring with oral Mn ingestion. The slight lowering effect of dietary wheat bran on tissue Mn deposition in chicks receiving Mn via intraperitoneal injection probably resulted from wheat bran inhibiting reabsorption of Mn of biliary and pancreatic origin. It would seem, therefore, that the gut is the primary site of action of the adverse effect of wheat bran on Mn homeostasis in the chick.

A subsequent experiment (9) was conducted to determine which chemical fraction in wheat bran, fish meal, rice bran and a corn-soybean meal mixture is responsible for the reduced Mn absorption. The neutral detergent fiber fraction in both wheat bran and the corn-soybean meal mixture reduced tissue Mn concentrations to the same extent as the intact feed ingredients. However, the ash component was responsible for the Mn-lowering effect of fish meal, and both the ash and neutral detergent fiber fractions of rice bran reduced tissue Mn concentrations, but not to the extent of intact rice bran. This study, although inconclusive, indicates that the fiber (NDF) component of some feedstuffs and the mineral (ash) component of others have a negative impact on Mn homeostasis in chicks. Harmuth-Hoene and Schelenz (10) have recently revealed a number of possible mechanisms by which fiber could interfere with mineral absorption. van der Aar and associates (11) have also reported that dietary fiber reduces mineral availability in chicks.

Phytate has been studied extensively with regard to mineral (mostly Zn and Ca) status of animals, and it has been shown to reduce whole-body Mn retention in rats (12). Phytate, however, is not present in the neutral detergent fiber or in the ash component of feedstuffs. Therefore, phytate does not appear to be responsible for the reduction of Mn uptake in chicks fed corn, soybean meal, wheat bran or fish meal (9). That phytate negatively impacts Mn nutriture also disagrees with the research of Reinhold et al. (13), who reported that fiber, and not phytate, was the primary factor determining bioavailability of divalent mineral elements in breads.

Inorganic Mn Supplements. The bioavailability of inorganic Mn supplements has been studied longer and more extensively than the bioavailability of Mn in feed ingredients. As early as 1939, Gallup and Norris (14) added 50 ppm Mn as $MnCl_2 \cdot 4H_2O$, $MnSO_4 \cdot 4H_2O$, $KMnO_4$, $MnCO_3$ or as MnO_2 to a conventional poultry diet and reported that the different Mn sources were equally efficacious in preventing perosis in chicks. Their high level of Mn supplementation (50 ppm), however, may have precluded the possibility of detecting small differences between the compounds. Hennig and coworkers (15), using uptake of radiolabeled Mn later reported that $MnCL_2$ was more available to the chick than $MnSO_4$ or MnO_2. Watson et al. (16) in 1970 described a growth and tissue Mn uptake technique for assessing Mn bioavailability of inorganic supplements. These researchers subsequently reported (17) that differences in Mn bioavailability existed between different sources of feedgrade Mn oxide and between feedgrade and reagent-grade Mn carbonate. Manganese oxide and Mn carbonate, depending on the source, however, were as available as $MnSO_4 \cdot H_2O$. In addition, these researchers reported that bone Mn concentration was more reflective of dietary Mn content than growth or bone ash percent, and that bone Mn concentration increased incrementally as dietary Mn concentrations increased between 10 and 120 ppm. Southern and Baker (18) compared the bioavailability of $MnSO_4 \cdot H_2O$, $MnCL_2 \cdot 4H_2O$, $MnCO_3$ and MnO_2 by adding excess Mn (3000, 4000 or 5000 ppm) to a corn-soybean meal diet and then measuring tissue Mn uptake, liver Fe accumulation, blood hemoglobin and hematocrit, as well as growth and feed efficiency. From these data, it was concluded that $MnSO_4 \cdot H_2O$, $MnCL_2 \cdot 4H_2O$ and $MnCO_3$ were more efficacious sources of Mn than MnO_2, and that $MnCO_3$ was slightly less efficacious than $MnSO_4 \cdot H_2O$ and $MnCL_2 \cdot 4H_2O$. Estimates of bioavailability were made using the slope-ratio technique. Assigning a value of 100% to $MnSO_4 \cdot H_2O$, availability estimates were 102, 77 and 29% for $MnCL_2 \cdot 4H_2O$, $MnCO_3$ and MnO_2, respectively. Black and associates (19) used a similar experimental design (1000, 2000 or 4000 ppm excess Mn) and determined the bioavailability of Mn in MnO and $MnCO_3$ relative to $MnSO_4 \cdot H_2O$. Bioavailability estimates, again using the slope-ratio technique, were 32 and 60% for $MnCO_3$ and MnO, respectively. Similarly, Henry et al. (20) reported that the Mn in MnO was 66% available compared with 100% for $MnSO_4 \cdot H_2O$. Manganese levels used in this investigation were 40, 80 and 120 ppm added to a corn-soybean meal diet.

Tissue Mn: Storage and Turnover

Storage. From the discussion of Mn bioavailability, it is obvious that dietary Mn intake is accurately reflected in tissue
Mn concentration in the chick. This is not surprising in that
most minerals are deposited into target tissues to some degree.
What is surprising, however, is the remarkable consistency with
which increments of dietary Mn, regardless of the concentration,
are deposited into certain tissues. Southern and Baker (18,21)
reported linear increases in bone and gallbladder Mn concentration in chicks fed 0, 1500 or 3000 ppm Mn (21) and in bile concentration in chicks fed 3000, 4000 or 5000 ppm Mn (18). Similarly, Black and coworkers (22) reported that dietary supplements of 0, 1000, 2000 and 3000 ppm Mn linearly increased Mn
concentration in liver, kidney, muscle, bone and plasma with
correlation coefficients (r) of .832, .933, .642, .974 and .893,
respectively. Black and coworkers (23) extended these findings
to account for length of time of Mn feeding (either 1, 2 or 3
weeks). Chicks were fed 0, 1000, 2000 or 3000 ppm Mn and killed
at one, two or three weeks after initiation of treatment diets.
Multiple regression analysis accounting for time of Mn feeding
and dietary Mn concentration revealed linear increases in liver
(.915), kidney (.980), pancreas (.931), muscle (.945), bone
(.987) and plasma (.969) Mn concentrations (correlations coefficients in parentheses).

Tissue Mn concentrations are not only responsive to high
dietary Mn levels, but also to dietary Mn levels near the chick's
requirement. Watson and coworkers (16-17) reported that bone Mn
responded linearly to dietary supplements of 0 to 120 ppm Mn.
This finding was later confirmed by Southern and Baker (21) and
by Henry et al. (20), and the responsive tissues were expanded
to include bone and kidney. Remarkably, slope (tissue Mn concentration regressed on Mn intake) was the same between 0 and 100
ppm dietary Mn as that occurring between 100 and 1000 ppm Mn.

Turnover and Utilization. There is little doubt that chicks fed
excess levels of Mn deposit this mineral in various body
tissues. Halpin (24) investigated the capacity of the chick to
remove this Mn from stored deposits and to use it for normal
bodily functions. Chicks were fed either 14 or 2000 ppm Mn in a
casein-dextrose diet for two weeks (8 to 22 days posthatching).
All chicks fed 2000 ppm Mn were then switched to 14 ppm Mn and
serially killed on days 0, 3, 7, 10 and 14 following the diet
switch. Tissue Mn concentrations are presented in Table I.
Depletion of tissue Mn was curvilinear with time. Log-transfor-
mation of the data, however, revealed a linear (P<.01) reduction
in Mn concentration in each of the tissues. Half-life (the number of days required to attain one-half of the initial tissue Mn
concentration) of the tissue Mn determined by regression analysis
on the log-transformed data was 6.0, 7.3 and 1.1 days in bone,
pancreas and bile, respectively. Suso and Edwards (25) obtained
a whole-body biological half-life of 5 days in chicks administered
^{54}Mn orally. From these investigations, it is clear that tissue

Table I. Tissue Mn Depletion[1]

Depletion Time Days	Tissue Mn Concentration, µg/g dry tissue		
	Bone	Pancreas	Bile
Experimental Chicks[2]			
0	49.5^g	25.4^d	205.7^e
3	35.3^f	13.2^{bc}	49.8^d
7	19.2^e	10.8^b	12.8^c
10	16.0^d	14.3^c	13.7^c
14	11.1^c	7.6^a	4.6^b
Control Chicks[2]			
0	3.5^b	7.8^a	4.4^b
14	2.4^a	5.9^a	0.1^a

[1]Means within a column not sharing a common superscript differ (P<.05). [2]Experimental chicks were fed 2000 ppm Mn during the 14-day pretest period and then switched to 14 ppm Mn during the 14-day depletion period. Control chicks were fed 14 ppm Mn throughout the 14-day pretest period and the 14-day depletion period.

stores of Mn are not inert and that they represent a labile pool of Mn for the chick.

Subsequent research at the University of Illinois (D.E. Laurin, K.M. Halpin and D.H. Baker, unpublished data) was conducted to assess the chick's ability to utilize stored Mn. Chick growth and tissue Mn concentration were determined in chicks fed a casein-dextrose, Mn-deficient diet after having previously been fed diets containing 14, 140 or 1400 ppm Mn from 0 to 8 days posthatching. Chicks fed pretest diets containing 14, 140 or 1400 ppm Mn required 14, 21 and 28 days of consuming the Mn-deficient diet, respectively, before they exhibited a Mn-deficient growth depression. Moreover, in chicks killed at the first sign of growth depression, bone and bile Mn concentrations were nearly identical to those of chicks fed the diet containing 14 ppm Mn throughout the study. Bone Mn concentrations dropped from their day-8 levels of 11, 28 and 167 µg/g ash to 3.0, 2.6 and 2.1 µg/g ash for chicks fed 14, 140 and 1400 ppm Mn during the first 8 days posthatching, respectively. Bone Mn concentrations of chicks fed the 14 ppm diet throughout the study were 11.6 and 3.0 ppm at days 8 and 36, respectively. These results indicate that chicks can utilize stored Mn to maintain optimum growth when placed on a Mn-deficient diet and that optimum growth will be maintained until body Mn stores are depleted.

Absorption

A poor absorption rate of Mn was thought to be one of the reasons for the high Mn requirement in poultry relative to mammals (2). Suso and Edwards (25) fed chicks a corn-soybean meal diet containing 79 ppm Mn or this diet supplemented with 55 or 110 ppm Mn from $MnSO_4 \cdot H_2O$. Chicks were dosed with .2 uCi. of ^{54}Mn, and Mn absorption efficiencies of 2.3, 2.1 and 1.5% were obtained for the basal (B), B+55 ppm Mn and B+110 ppm Mn diets, respectively. Turk and associates (26), also using a corn-soybean meal diet (104 ppm Mn), but 2 uCi. of ^{54}Mn from $MnCl_2$, reported a Mn absorption efficiency of .00819%. Halpin, Chausow and Baker (27) compared Mn absorption efficiencies in chicks fed a conventional poultry diet (corn-soybean meal, 30 ppm Mn, no inorganic Mn supplementation) or a casein-dextrose diet essentially devoid in fiber and excess nutrients. Absorption efficiencies were determined by using the slope-ratio procedure to compare bone Mn deposition in chicks dosed orally with increasing increments of Mn with that of chicks injected intraperitoneally with increasing increments of Mn. The absorption efficiency of Mn was 1.71% in the corn-soybean meal diet and 2.40% in the casein-dextrose diet. The estimate of 1.71% efficiency is lower than the estimate of Suso and Edwards (25), but considerably higher than the estimate of Turk (26). In addition, Suso and Edwards (25) reported a reduced rate of Mn absorption as a result of inorganic Mn supplementation. This is contrary to the fact that bone Mn increases linearly as dietary Mn intake increases over a wide range (see Tissue Mn: Storage and Turnover). In fact, Halpin et al. (27) reported that regression of bone Mn concentration on 14-day Mn intakes was linear, with coefficients of determination (r^2) ranging from .95-1.00.

The data on absorption efficiency of Mn are by no means consistent, but efficiency is probably in the range of one to three percent depending on the type of diet and on the presence or absence of dietary Mn antagonists (eg., ash or fiber). This range of absorption efficiencies in the chick is not greatly different from estimates of one to four percent made in mammals (28-29). Thus, the chick's high Mn requirement relative to mammals is probably not totally a result of inefficient Mn absorption. Instead, avians may experience a more rapid turnover of stored Mn than mammals, although more definitive data are needed to verify this hypothesis.

Interactions with Minerals

Microminerals. Manganese probably interacts to some extent with many trace elements depending on the concentration of Mn and on the concentration of the other interactive element. Other dietary constituents probably play a role as well. The discussion here, however, will be limited to the interaction of Mn with Co and Fe. Thomson and Valberg (30) perfused test solutions of Fe, Co and Mn into open-ended duodenal loops of rats and reported that Mn uptake was inhibited by both Co and Fe, and that Mn inhibited uptake of these minerals in return. In a preliminary investigation, Halpin and Baker (31) reported that Co did not inhibit Mn uptake, but instead, 1000 ppm dietary Co increased tissue Mn deposition. This finding was later confirmed by Brown and Southern (32) and by Halpin (24). The investigations by Halpin and Baker (31) and by Brown and Southern (32) were conducted using a corn-soybean meal diet. It was originally thought that Co increased Mn uptake by competitively binding to dietary factors that might otherwise bind Mn. In the report by Halpin (24), however, the positive effect of Co on Mn uptake was evident even in a casein-dextrose diet devoid of fiber and containing a minimum of excess nutrients. It would therefore appear that the Mn-binding properties of the corn-soybean meal diet were not completely responsible for the Co-induced enhancement of Mn uptake.

An interaction also exists between Fe and Mn at the gut level in rats (30), and it has been established numerous times that excess supplemental Mn adversely affects Fe status of mammals and chicks (2,18,21). Halpin (24) recently investigated the mutual interrelationship between Mn and Fe in chicks. In a casein-dextrose diet containing either 14 or 1014 ppm Mn, Fe ranging from deficient to a 2000 ppm excess had little or no effect on chick gain or on tissue Mn concentration. The 1000 ppm Mn addition, however, reduced hemoglobin and hematocrit levels when dietary Fe was at or below the chick's requirement. These data indicate that the interrelationship between Fe and Mn is unidirectional in chicks; ie., excess Mn affects Fe status of chicks, but excess Fe does not affect Mn status of chicks. Therefore, this interaction appears to be similar to the unidirectional interactions between Fe and Zn (33) and between Zn and Cu (34-35).

Macrominerals. The effect of Ca and P on Mn nutriture of chicks has been an area of investigation since Mn supplements were first shown to prevent perosis in chicks. Schaible and Bandemer (36) reported that excesses of bone meal or of $Ca_3(PO_4)_2$ reduced Mn availability and precipitated Mn deficiency. More recently, high dietary Ca (2 and 3%) was shown to reduce Mn utilization; the incidence of perosis was increased and tissue Mn concentrations were decreased by excess Ca (37). Unpublished data from the University of Illinois revealed that 3% $CaCO_3$ reduced chick gain, feed efficiency and bile Mn concentration, but it had no effect on bone Mn level. Moreover, the adverse effects of $CaCO_3$ were not alleviated by Mn supplementation. This would indicate that the adverse effects of $CaCO_3$ were not mediated by a Ca-induced Mn deficiency. The early research of Schaible and Bandemer (36) and the more recent investigation of Smith and Kabaija (37) were conducted using oyster shell flour to vary Ca levels. The research at the University of Illinois used limestone to increase Ca content of the experimental diets. Dissimilarities in micromineral profiles, or macromineral for that matter, of the two ingredients could account for these disparate results. Nonetheless, more research is needed to absolve the interaction between Ca and Mn.

Interaction with Coccidiosis

Coccidial infections resulting from infections by Eimeria acervulina (duodenal coccidiosis) have been shown to affect nutrient absorption (21,26,35,38). Turk et al. (26), using radiolabeled Mn, reported that experimental E. acervulina infection decreased Mn absorption during the acute phase of infection (6 days postinoculation), but that the infection increased Mn absorption during the recovery period. Southern and Baker (32) and Brown and Southern (21) reported that chronic E. acervulina infection increased Mn absorption. Bone and bile Mn concentrations were increased and signs of Mn toxicosis symptoms, as assessed hematologically, were exacerbated by the infection. The rate of bone Mn uptake was nearly doubled, and the Mn requirement of coccidiosis-infected chicks was reduced. Thus, E. acervulina infection clearly increased Mn absorption and/or retention.

Requirement and Toxicity

Requirement. The Mn requirement of chicks fed a casein-dextrose diet low in fiber, phytate and excess nutrients is 14 ppm (7,21). The National Research Council (39) has set a requirement of 60 ppm in conventional poultry diets. Because of the potential negative effect of conventional feedstuffs (see Bioavailability Section) on Mn bioavailability, the estimate of 60 ppm seems appropriate.

Toxicity. The toxicity of Mn for chicks was recently reviewed (40). Signs of toxicosis have been shown to vary depending on type of diet used, mineral composition of the diet and on source of Mn. Heller and Penquite (41) reported that 4779 ppm Mn from $MnCO_3$ reduced chick growth and caused 52% mortality. More recently, similar levels of Mn were fed to chicks with only mild anemia and a slight growth depression observed (18,19,22). Without a definitive Mn toxicity trial, it is difficult to comment specifically on Mn toxicosis in chicks. Generally though, high levels of Mn are tolerated well by chicks, especially in conventional poultry diets.

Literature Cited

1. Wilgus Jr., H. S.; Norris, L. C.; Heuser, G. F. Science 1936, 84, 252-53.
2. Underwood, E. J. Trace Elements in Human and Animal Nutrition; Academic Press: New York, 1977; Chapter 7.
3. Davis, P. N.; Norris, L. C.; Kratzer, F. H. J. Nutr. 1962, 77, 217-23.
4. Holmes, W. B.; Roberts, R. Poultry Sci. 1963, 42, 803-9.
5. Seth, P. C. C.; Clandinin, D. R. Poultry Sci. 1973, 52, 1158-60.
6. Halpin, K. M.; Baker, D. H. Poultry Sci. 1986, 65, 995-1003.

7. Halpin, K. M.; Baker, D. H. Poultry Sci. 1986, 65, 1371-74.
8. Thompson, S. A.; Weber, C. W. Poultry Sci. 1981, 60, 840-45.
9. Halpin, K. M.; Baker, D. H. Poultry Sci. 1986, 64 Supplement 1, 111 (Abstr.).
10. Harmuth-Hoene, A.; Schelenz, R. J. Nutr. 1980, 110, 1774-84.
11. van der Aar, P. J.; Fahey, G. C., Jr.; Ricke, S. C.; Allen, S. E.; Berger, L. L. J. Nutr. 1983, 113, 653-61.
12. Davis, N. T.; Nightingale, R. Br. J. Nutr. 1975, 34, 243-58.
13. Reinhold, J. G.; Ismail-Beigi, F.; Faradji, B. Nutr. Rep. Int. 1975, 12, 75-85.
14. Gallup, W. D.; Norris, L. C. Poultry Sci. 1939, 18, 76-82.
15. Hennig, A.; Anke, M.; Jeroch, H.; Kaltwasser, W.; Weidner, G.; Hoffman, G.; Diettrich, M.; Marcy, H. Biol. Abstr. 1976, 45, 75618.
16. Watson, L. T.; Ammerman, C. B.; Miller, S. M.; Harms, R. H. Poultry Sci. 1970, 49, 1548-54.
17. Watson, L. T.; Ammerman, C. B.; Miller, S. M.; Harms, R. H. Poultry Sci. 1971, 50, 1693-1700.
18. Southern, L. L.; Baker, D. H. Poultry Sci. 1983, 62, 642-46.
19. Black, J. R.; Ammerman, C. B.; Henry, P. R.; Miles, R. D. Poultry Sci. 1984, 63, 1999-2006.
20. Henry, P. R.; Ammerman, C. B.; Miles, R. D. Poultry Sci. 1986, 65, 983-86.
21. Southern, L. L.; Baker, D. H. J. Nutr. 1983, 113, 172-77.
22. Black, J. R.; Ammerman, C. B.; Henry, P. R.; Miles, R. D. Nutr. Rep. Int. 1984, 29, 807-14.
23. Black, J. R.; Ammerman, C. B.; Henry, P. R.; Miles, R. D. Poultry Sci. 1985, 64, 688-93.
24. Halpin, K. M. Ph.D. Thesis, University of Illinois, Illinois, 1985.
25. Suso, F. A.; Edwards, H. M., Jr. Poultry Sci. 1968, 48, 933-38.
26. Turk, D. E.; Gunji, D. S.; Molitoris, P. Poultry Sci. 1982, 61, 2430-34.
27. Halpin, K. M.; Chausow, D. G.; Baker, D. H. J. Nutr. 1986, 116, 1747-51.
28. Greenburg, D. M.; Copp, D. H.; Cuthbertson, E. M. J. Biol. Chem. 1944, 147, 749-56.
29. Sansom, B. F.; Gibbons, S. N.; Dixon, A. M.; Russell, A. M.; Symonds, H. W. In Nuclear Techniques in Animal Production and Health; International Atomic Energy Agency; Viena, 1976; p 179-189.
30. Thompson, A. B. R.; Valberg, L. S. Amer. J. Phys. 1972, 223, 1327-29.
31. Halpin, K. M.; Baker, D. H. Poultry Sci. 1984, 63, 109 (Abstr.).
32. Brown, D. R.; Southern, L. L. J. Nutr. 1985, 115, 347-51.
33. Bafundo, K. W.; Baker, D. H.; Fitzgerald, P. R. J. Nutr. 1984, 114, 1306-12.

34. O'Dell, B. L.; Reeves, P. G.; Morgan, R. F. In Trace Substances in Environmental Health; University of Missouri, Columbia, 1976; p 411-21.
35. Southern, L. L.; Baker, D. H. J. Nutr. 1983, 113, 688-96.
36. Schaible, P. J.; Bandemer, S. L. Poultry Sci. 1942, 21, 8-14.
37. Smith, O. B.; Kabaija, E. Poultry Sci. 1985, 64, 1713-20.
38. Turk, D. E. Fed. Proc. 1974, 33, 106-11.
39. National Research Council; Nutrient Requirements of Poultry; National Academy of Sciences; Washington, DC, 1984.
40. Mineral Tolerances of Domestic Animals; National Academy of Sciences; Washington, DC, 1980; p 290-303.
41. Heller, V. G.; Penquite, R. Poultry Sci. 1937, 16, 243-46.

RECEIVED January 28, 1987

Chapter 5

Role of Manganese in Bone Metabolism

Linda Strause and Paul Saltman

Department of Biology (B-022), University of California—San Diego,
La Jolla, CA 92093

The role of trace elements in general, and Mn(II) in particular, has been examined in the metabolism of calcified
tissue at several levels. The tissue distribution of
^{54}Mn orally administered to mice was followed. Specific
Mn(II) binding sites in the enamel of teeth have been
characterized using EPR. Rats on long-term, 12-24
months, dietary regimens depleted in Mn or low Mn-low Cu
showed significantly lower bone density and higher serum
Ca than controls. The application of ectopic subcutaneous implants of bone powder and demineralized bone powder
into animals on control or Mn deplete diets demonstrated
that osteoblast activity, a measure of bone formation,
was impaired as was osteoclast activity, a parameter of
bone resorption. The multiple cellular effects of Mn
deficiency include: decreased bone resorption, production
of labile bone, and decreased synthesis of organic
matrix. The serum level of Mn in a group of osteoporotic
postmenopausal women was significantly lower than age-
matched controls.

Our interest in the role of trace elements in bone metabolism
developed in a rather bizarre fashion. We became interested in the
orthopedic problems of a prominent professional basketball player,
Bill Walton. Several years ago he was plagued by frequent broken
bones, pains in his joints and an inability to heal bone fractures.
We hypothesized that he might be deficient in trace elements as a
result of his very limited vegetarian diet. In cooperation with his
physician, we were able to analyze Walton's serum. We found no
detectable manganese (Mn). His serum concentrations of copper (Cu)
and zinc (Zn) were below normal values. Dietary supplementation with
trace elements and calcium (Ca) was begun. Over a period of several
months his bones healed and he returned to professional basketball
(1,2). In cooperation with several other orthopedic physicians, we
analyzed serum from other patients with slow bone healing. Several
of these patients also had abnormally low Zn, Cu and Mn levels.

0097-6156/87/0354-0046$06.00/0

It comes as no great surprise that trace elements may affect the growth and development of bone. Trace element deficiences profoundly alter bone metabolism in animals either directly or indirectly (3). The absence of a trace element in the diet can lead to inefficient functioning of a specific enzyme or enzymes that require the transition element as a cofactor. An example of this is the role of Cu and iron (Fe) in the cross-linking of collagen and elastins (4-9). The participation of Mn in the biosynthesis of mucopolysaccharides (10-12) is another example. Zn deficiency causes a reduction in osteoblastic activity, collagen and chondroitin sulfate synthesis and alkaline phosphatase activity (13-16).

Hurley and her collaborators have studied the perosis (faulty tendons) induced by both Mn and Zn deficiencies (17-19). Previous workers have described skeletal abnormalities in chicks and rats including disproportionate growth of skeleton, bone rarefaction and chondrodystrophy, as overt manifestation of zinc deficiency (20,21). Hurley et al., were able to demonstrate that the metabolic lesion produced by Mn was quite different from that produced by the absence of Zn. In the case of Mn there was no alteration in the mineralization processes measured by the dynamics of radiocalcium movement. The influence of trace elements on in vitro tissue cultures of chick osteoblasts has been reported (22). Among the elements required were Fe, Cu, Zn and Mn.

Genetic models of trace element insufficiency are known in animals and humans. The mutation in mice called pallid produces conditions similar to those observed in prenatal Mn deficiency (17,23). There is an abnormal and delayed ossification of the otic capsule and failure of the otoliths to calcify. These conditions can be reversed by the application of therapeutic amounts of Mn to the pregnant female and into the diet of the offspring. Over the past several years we have sought to understand more thoroughly the metabolic factors which regulate and control trace element metabolism (24). We decided to combine and extend these interests to learn more about the mechanisms of uptake and transport of Mn and how that trace element may be involved in various aspects of bone metabolism. In this review we trace the progress we have made with respect to transport and distribution of Mn in the mouse, the development of a model of osteopenia in the rat induced by trace element deficiencies, an investigation of the role of Mn in osteoclast and osteoblast activity in the rat, and ultimately describe some new clinical findings which indicate that Mn deficiency may have a significant role in osteoporosis.

Studies of Manganese Uptake and Distribution by the Mouse

Relatively little attention has been paid to the mechanisms by which Mn is absorbed from the diet. Most studies have used intraperitoneal or intravenous injections of ^{54}Mn(II) salts (25,26). In vitro studies using intestinal segments suggested that membrane transport carriers might be involved, but also that complexation of the metal influences transport (27). The hydrolysis of the transition metal ions strongly influences their ability to cross various biological membranes. The presence of low molecular weight organic chelating agents both of a dietary origin or synthetic complexing agents with specific chemical affinities could alter both the rate of transport and distribution of the metal ion absorbed. Using the technique of whole body counting to follow the retention of a single dose of radioactive Mn administered per os, we intubated either $^{54}MnCl_2$ or $^{54}Mn-NTA$ (nitrilotriacetic acid) into mice (28). The cumulative retention was followed for a period of 10 days (Figure 1). No significant difference was seen with or without the chelating agent. It is interesting to note that less than 3% of the total dose administered was retained after 10 days.

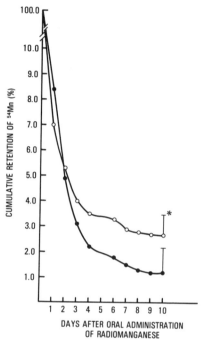

Figure 1. Percent daily retention of a single oral dose of $^{54}MnCl_2$ (o) at pH 2 and $^{54}MnNTA$ (●) at pH 9 (28). Each datum point for whole body retention represents the average 25 individual animals. * = $p < 0.01$. (Reproduced with permission from ref. 28. Copyright 1985 The Humana Press.)

Distribution of ^{54}Mn in various tissues was determined 10 days after administration of the isotopes. Animals were killed by CO_2 asphyxiation. Heart, spleen, femur, gastrocnemius muscle and portions of the liver and small intestine were removed and weighed. Blood was collected by heart puncture. Initially it appeared that $MnCl_2$ was more effectively absorbed than Mn-NTA. However the entire difference between the two forms administered could be accounted for by the rapid and persistent adsorption of the Mn onto the teeth when fed as the ionic salt. When corrected for adsorption to teeth, less than 1% of the $MnCl_2$ was absorbed by the animal. The greatest amount of radioactivity was accumulated in the muscle mass and liver. Approximately 10% was found in the bone.

The rapid loss of radioisotope following a single oral dose suggests that the intestine is the major component in the regulation of Mn absorption. Our finding of a very low efficiency of mucosa to serosa transfer of Mn is consistent with the studies of Thompson and Valberg (29,30). They demonstrated that approximately 25% of the Mn taken up in the mucosal cells is transferred to the carcass.

We were intrigued by the very tight binding of Mn to the surface of the teeth in mice. A series of teeth from the lower jaw of mice intubated with ^{54}MnCl$_2$ solution were removed and examined by electron paramagnetic resonance. With the cooperation of Dr. Dennis Chasteen of the Department of Chemistry at the University of New Hampshire, we concluded that Mn appears to substitute for Ca within the hydroxyapatite structure of the tooth. In such a site, the Mn is probably coordinated to six phosphate groups. Mn is not simply surface adsorbed. It seems to penetrate the tooth and is tenaciously bound. Similar studies with chemically prepared hydroxyapatite crystals exposed to Mn(II) revealed a significantly different ligand environment than the tooth enamel itself. Further experiments are underway to understand how binding of Mn(II) to teeth and bone might be exploited in linking various compounds to the surface of hard tissue.

A Model of Osteopenia Produced in the Rat by Deficiencies in Mn and Cu.

We have developed a semi-synthetic animal diet in which the levels of trace elements can be carefully controlled (31). We selected three dietary conditions: control (C) 66 ppm Mn and 5ppm Cu; low-Mn low-Cu (L) 2.5 ppm Mn and 0.5 ppm Cu; and Mn-deplete (D) no added Mn and 5 ppm Cu. Female Sprague Dawley rats were randomly divided at weaning into the three dietary groups. Food and distilled water were provided ad libitum for the entire experimental period of twelve months. The weight gain of all animals was approximately the same.

Five animals from each group were killed by CO_2 asphyxiation after a 12-hour overnight period of starvation. Animals were killed at 2, 13, 26, and 52 weeks after the start of the dietary regimen. Various tissues were sampled, immediately frozen in liquid nitrogen and stored at $-80^{\circ}C$. Trace element determinations were made on all tissue and sera following digestion in concentrated nitric acid using high-pressure Teflon chambers (31). Ca, Cu, and Zn were determined by flame atomic absorption spectrophotometry. Mn was measured using electrothermal atomic absorption spectrophotometry. Isolated humeri from eight animals per dietary group were X-rayed.

Mineral levels in serum and bone from rats on the 3 different diets are shown in Table I. Serum Ca was significantly higher in deficient rats at six months. Serum Cu and Mn were significantly lower in L and D rats respectively. The mineral concentrations of Ca in the femur as well as Mn were affected by the Mn-deficient diets. Ca concentrations of the femur was inversely correlated with the serum Ca concentrations in the L and D rats. Radiographic observations of isolated humeri indicated that osteopenic-like lesions were associated with the L and D regimens (31).

Table I. Mineral Levels in Serum and Bone from Rats Fed
Three Different Diets for 12 mo[1,2]

Measure	Diets		
	N	L	D
Serum (6)			
Ca, mg/L	103 ± 15[a]	119 ± 16[ab]	134 ± 15[b]
P, mg/L	39 ± 1[a]	63 ± 4[b]	50 ± 3[c]
Cu, mg/L	1.2 ± 0.6[a]	0.08 ± 0.05[b]	1.2 ± 0.3[a]
Mn, mg/L	0.08 ± 0.05[a]	0.03 ± 0.02[a]	0.03 ± 0.02[a]
Zn, mg/L	1.0 ± 0.3[a]	1.1 ± 0.3[a]	1.2 ± 0.3[a]
Femur (6)			
Ca, mg/g	272 ± 60[a]	221 ± 30[ab]	180 ± 16[b]
P, mg/g	167 ± 14[a]	156 ± 9[a]	155 ± 20[a]
Cu, μg/g	1.46 ± 0.55[a]	0.71 ± 0.45[a]	0.95 ± 0.40[a]
Mn, μg/g	2.70 ± 1.5[a]	1.03 ± 0.14[ab]	0.95 ± 0.80[b]
Zn, μg/g	282 ± 30[a]	283 ± 31[a]	259 ± 32[a]

[1]Values are means ± SD for the number of rats per group in parentheses.
[2]Within a row, means not sharing a common superscript are significantly different (P < 0.05) by Student's two-tailed unpaired t-test.

Insufficient intakes of Mn and Cu resulted in significant abnormalities in both serum and bone mineral levels within twelve months. Why a chronic deficiency of trace elements should result in conditions of osteopenia is not at present clear. It has been suggested that osteopenia is associated with an increased rate of bone resorption (33). Others have implicated decreased bone formation or osteoblast activity in some forms of osteoporosis (34). What is obviously at issue is a balance between the rate of bone resorption and that of bone synthesis (35-37). How that equilibrium dynamic is affected by trace elements will be discussed below.

The Effect of Mn and Cu Deficiencies on Osteo-Induction and Resorption of Bone Particles in Rats

One of the most sensitive bioassays for osteoblast and osteoclast activities in vivo is the use of ectopic models of bone formation and bone matrix resorption (38,39). Devitalized, demineralized bone powders (DBP) are subcutaneously implanted in young rats. There is a phenotypic conversion of connective cell tissue mesenchyme into cartilage. Subsequently this cartilage becomes calcified, vascularized and bone is deposited in two weeks. If mineral-containing bone particles (BP) are implanted, a different phenomenon is observed. Large multinucleated osteoclast-like cells are recruited to the site of implantation. There is a complete resorption of the BP four weeks after implantation. In collaboration with Dr. Julie Glowacki of the Harvard University School of Medicine, we took advantage of these procedures and used implants of normal DBP and BP into rats that had been maintained on the three experimental diets: C, L, and D (40).

Isogenic bone powder was prepared from femurs, humeri and tibia of normal adult rats. The clean diaphyses were extracted with absolute ethanol followed by anhydrous ethyl ether. Bones were pulverized in a liquid nitrogen impacting mill and sieved to particle sizes between 75 to 250 μm. The demineralized powder was prepared by extracting BP with 0.5 M HCl for three hours at room temperature followed by extensive washes in distilled water to remove all acid and minerals. Sequential washes with absolute ethanol and finally with anhydrous ether prepared the dry powder. Bilateral subcutaneous pockets in the thoracic area in anesthetized rats were implanted with either DBP or BP. Sets of six pellets were harvested from animals under each of the dietary conditions at 2, 6 and 17 weeks following implantation of the DBP. Implants of the BP were harvested at 2 and 4 weeks following implantation.

Pellets were removed and prepared for histological examination as previously described (37). An arbitrary "induction index", defined as the mean fractional area represented by induced cartilage, (IC) and induced bone (IB), was used to characterize the elicitation of osteoblastic activity by the DBP. A summary of the results of these experiments is presented in Table II. At 6 and 17 weeks following implantation of the DBP significant bone formation is observed in the C rats. No cartilage was apparent in the 2 week specimens from the L rats. At 6 and 17 weeks some induced bone was present. At no time throughout the course of experiments did the DBP elicit formation of either cartilage or bone in the Mn-deplete rats.

Table II.   Induction Index from Normal DBP Implanted into Test Rats Maintained on Experimental Diets for 6 months (40) [a]

Weeks After Implantation	DIET		
	CONTROL	LOW	DEPLETE
2	12.7(IC)	0	0
6	41.5(IB)	49.5(IC+IB)	0
17	31.3(IB)	20.0(IB)	0

[a] Induction Index is the mean fractional histomorphometric area represented by induced cartilage (IC) or induced bone (IB) x 10^3.

Table III presents the results of BP implants into the 3 different groups of rats. The percentage of implanted BP particles resorbed per microscopic field was used as a measure of osteoclast induction. The decrease in relative resorption of BP in the L and D rats is apparent. Deficiencies in Mn and Cu appear to decrease osteoclast activity.

The implantation experiments correlate well with the observations for skeletal development under the three dietary conditions. The osteopenia observed in the rats raised for 12 months on the L or D diets could be a manifestation of a disequilibrium between the rates of osteoclastic and osteoblastic activity. Both of these cellular activities are influenced by the trace element status of the animal. If the osteoblastic activity were more strongly inhibited by

Table III. Resorption of Normal Bone Particles (BP) in Test
Rats Maintained on Experimental Diets (40) [a]

DIET	N	BP (Area/Field)	%BP Resorbed	Relative Resorption
CONTROL	5	4584 ± 528	46.2	100%
LOW	6	7203 ± 612	15.4	33%[b]
DEPLETE	5	7451 ± 482	12.4	27%[b]

[a]Specimens harvested at 14 d after implantation of BP into rats maintained on diets for 12 months.
[b]Significantly different (P<.01) from control group by Student's two-tailed unpaired t-test corrected for multiple comparisons.

the deficiencies than the osteoclastic activity a net loss of bone would be expected.

It has been shown that Mn-deficient hens and rats show disproportionate growth of skeletons and under-glycosylation of proteoglycans (41,42). Lysyloxidase, a Cu-requiring enzyme, is essential for the cross-linking of elastin and collagen (5,43). We carried out a study in which the ectopic implants were prepared from bones of animals raised on the different dietary regimens to characterize possible changes in their structure and activity. Bone powders were prepared from rats raised for 12 months on one of the three diets: L or D. The BP was implanted into normal 28-day-old rats. The lability of the BP's to the mobilized osteoclasts was measured. Preliminary experiments indicate that BP's from the L and D rats were significantly more labile than those from the C rats, 121%, 123%, and 100%, respectively. At this time we are unable to determine whether Mn and Cu deficiency yields a bone less resistant to osteoclast attack, or that more osteoclasts are mobilized.

We measured cell number and osteonectin concentration using fetal calvarial cultures from control (C) and Mn-deplete (D) rats. We hypothesized that Mn deficiency may result in the under-glycosylation of osteonectin. Preliminary experiments showed an increase in osteoblast cell number in cultures from C rats as compared to D rats, 0.677×10^6 and 0.229×10^6, respectively. Osteonectin level was lower in C cultures than in D cultures, 181 ng/10^6 cells and 995 ng/10^6 cells, respectively. When Mn was added to the media of both C and D cultures, osteonectin levels increased, 221 ng/10^6 cells and 1027 ng/10^6 cells, respectively. In primary osteoblast cultures it is speculated that if cells are stimulated to divide, phenotypic markers may actually decrease. The higher level of osteonectin in the D cultures may be due to the slower growth rate of these cells. A greater number of cells in the differentiation stage would result in proportionally greater synthesis of proteins such as osteonectin.

Proteoglycans are a small but significant component of the mineralized bone matrix. Proteoglycan content of humeral epiphyses from rats raised for six months on our D diet was estimated by measuring glycosaminoglycan (GAG) levels. Preliminary results showed a much greater GAG level in the C rats than in D rats. The total proteoglycan and bone-specific proteoglycan in C rat bones (2.19 µg/mg and 0.119 µg/mg, respectively) was greater than that in the D bones (1.43 µg/mg and 0.016 µg/mg, respectively). We observed a shift toward lowered bone density and a change in the mineralization profile of bone diaphyses in rats raised on the L and D diets for six months. No changes were detected in the control rats.

Clinical Correlations of Osteoporosis with Serum Manganese

In collaboration with Dr. Jean-Yves Reginster at the Medical School of the University of Liege, Belgium, we measured Ca, Cu, Mn and Zn concentrations in serum and bone samples from postmenopausal osteoporotic and age matched normal women. The osteoporotic patients were selected by the presence of at least one vertebral non-traumatic crush fracture. Normal subjects were selected on the basis of their bone mineral content and bone mineral density as measured by dual-photon-absorptiometry. There were significant differences between the osteoporotic and normal women in parameters of bone density. Serum Mn was significantly lower in osteoporotics (Table IV). No significant differences were found in the following: bone Cu, Mn, Zn, osteoid volume, osteoid surface, osteoclastic resorption surface; or serum Cu, Zn, bone Gla protein and 1,25 dihydroxy vitamin D3. For all subjects the trace elements (Cu, Mn and Fe) were within the normal range. We are not able to draw a definitive conclusion that serum Mn is directly related to the pathogenesis of osteoporosis. However, low serum Mn may be related to decreased bone mass as seen in experimental animals. It is necessary to carry out longitudinal studies in large populations of healthly post-menopausal women comparing the rate of bone loss to variations in serum concentrations of these trace elements.

Table IV. Bone and Serum Values in Osteoporotic and Normal Women

	Normal Subjects	Osteoporotic Patients
Bone Calcium (mg/g)	149.7 ± 17.3	113.7 ± 28.4 [***]
Trabecular Bone Volume (%)	23.4 ± 5.9	12.6 ± 1.7 [***]
Bone Mineral Content (g/cm)	5.7 ± 0.5	3.7 ± 0.5 [**]
Bone Mineral Density (g/cm^2)	1.0 ± 0.3	0.7 ± 0.1 [*]
Serum Manganese (mg/L)	0.04 ± 0.03	0.01 ± 0.004

[*] $P < 0.05$;   [**] $P < 0.01$;   [***] $P < 0.001$

There is a great deal of both popular and professional interest in the etiology, diagnosis, prevention, and treatment of osteoporosis. The extent of this disease in the United States is a major public health concern. No single cause can be identified. Certainly the influence of hormones, dietary intakes of Ca, fluoride and vitamin D are significant. Our results suggest that it may be prudent to consider the possibility that trace element deficiencies, particularly of Mn, may be of significance.

Acknowledgments

This work was supported in part by the USPHS NIH Research Grant AM-123 86 and a gift from the Proctor and Gamble Co.

Literature Cited

1. Gold, M. Science 80 1980, May/June 101–102.
2. Saltman, P. Anabolism 1984, 3, 7.
3. Asling, C.W.; Hurley, L.S. Clin. Orthopaedics 1963, 27, 213–264.
4. Carnes, W.H. Fed. Proc. 1971, 30, 995–1000.
5. Opsahl, W.; Zeronian, H.; Ellison, M.; Lewis, D.; Rucker, R.B.; Riggins, R.S. J. Nutr., 1982, 112, 708–716.
6. Rucker, R.B.; Riggins, R.S.; Laughlin, R.; Chan, M.M.; Chen, M.; Ton, K. J. Nutr. 1975, 105, 1062–1070.
7. Baxter, J.H. Am. J. Physiol. 1951, 167, 766.
8. O'Dell, B.L. Phil. Trans. R. Soc. Land. 1981, 294, 91–104.
9. Prockop, D.J. Fed. Proc. 1971, 30, 984–990.
10. Underwood, E.T. In Trace Elements in Human and Animal Nutrition 4th Edition; Academic Press: New York, 1977; pp 179.
11. Leach, R.M.; Muenster, A.M. J. Nutr. 1962, 78, 51–56.
12. Leach, R.M.; Muenster, A.M.; Wein, E. Arch. Biochem. Biophys. 1969, 133, 22–28.
13. Calhoun, N.R.; Smith, J.C.; Becker, K.L. Orthop. 1974, 103, 212–234.
14. Murray, E.J.; Langhaus, B., Messer, H.H. Nutr. Res. 1981, 1, 107–115.
15. Huber, A.M.; Gershoff, S.N. J. Nutr. 1973, 103, 1175–1181.
16. Westmoreland, N. Fed. Proc. 1971, 30, 1001–1010.
17. Hurley, L.S. In Developmental Nutrition; Prentice-Hall, Inc.: New Jersey, 1980; pp 199–227.
18. Hurley, L.S. Am. J. Clin. Nutr. 1969, 22, 1332–1339.
19. Beach, R.S.; Gershwin, M.E.; Hurley, L.S. J. Nutr., 1980, 110, 201–211.
20. O'Dell, B.O.; Newberne, P.M.; Lavage, J.E. J. Nutr. 1958, 65, 503–512.
21. Sanstead, H.H. In Present Knowledge in Nutrition, 4th Edition; Hegsted, D.M., Ed.; The Nutrition Foundation, Inc.: New York, 1976, pp 290–301.
22. Farley, J.R.; Baylink, D.J. Clin. Res. 1982, 30, 61.
23. Hurley, L.S.; Bell, L.T. J. Nutr. 1974, 104, 133–137.
24. Saltman, P; Hegenauer, J.; Strause, L. In Metabolism of Trace Metals in Man: Rennert, O.M.; Chan, W.Y., Eds.; CRC Press: Fl, 1984; Vol. 1, pp 1–16.
25. Britton, A.A.; Cotzias, G.C. Am. J. Physiol. 1966, 211, 203–206.
26. Papavasilious, P.S.; Miller, S.T.; Cotzias, G.C. Am. J. Physiol. 1966, 211, 211–216.
27. Garcia-Aranda, J.A.; Wapnir, R.A.; Lifshitz, F. J. Nutr. 1983, 113, 2601–2607.

28. Strause, L.; Hegenauer, J.; Burstein, D.; Saltman, P. <u>Biol.</u>
    <u>Trace</u> <u>Element</u> <u>Res.</u> 1985, <u>7</u>, 75–81.
29. Thomson, A.B.R.; Valberg, L.S. <u>Am.</u> <u>J.</u> <u>Physiol.</u> 1972,
    <u>233</u>, 1327–1329.
30. Thomson, A.B.R.; Olatunboson, D.; Valberg, L.S. <u>J.</u> <u>Lab.</u>
    <u>Clin.</u> <u>Med.</u> 1971, <u>78</u>, 642–655.
31. Strause, L.G.; Hegenauer, J.; Saltman, P.; Cone, R.;
    Resnick, D. <u>J.</u> <u>Nutr.</u> 1986, <u>116</u>, 135–141.
32. McKnight, R.; Saltman, P. <u>Analy.</u> <u>Biochem.</u> 1986, <u>157</u>,
    343–344.
33. Nordin, B.E.C.; Aaron, J.; Sepped, R.; Crilly, R.G. <u>Lancet</u>
    1981, <u>II</u>, 277–279.
34. Lips, P.; Courpron, P.; Meunier, P.J. <u>Calcif.</u> <u>Tissue</u> <u>Res.</u>
    1978, <u>26</u>, 13–17.
35. Riggs, B.L. <u>Mineral</u> <u>and</u> <u>Electrolyte</u> <u>Metab.</u> 1981, <u>5</u>, 265–275.
36. Parfitt, A.M. <u>Metab.</u> <u>bone</u> <u>Dis.</u> <u>and</u> <u>Rel.</u> <u>Res.</u> 1982, <u>4</u>, 1–6.
37. Howard, G.A.; Bottemiller, B.L.; Baylink, D.T. <u>Metab.</u>
    <u>Bone</u> <u>Dis.</u> <u>and</u> <u>Rel.</u> <u>Res.</u> 1980, <u>2</u>, 131–135.
38. Glowacki, J.; Altobelli, D., Mulliken, J.B. Inc: <u>Calcif.</u>
    <u>Tissue</u> <u>Internat.</u> 1981, <u>33</u>, 71–76.
39. Glowacki, T. In <u>Factors</u> <u>and</u> <u>Mechanisms</u> <u>Influencing</u> <u>Bone</u>
    <u>Growth</u>; Alan R. Liss, Inc: New York, 1982, pp 83–91.
40. Strause, L.; Glowacki, J.; Saltman, P. <u>Calcified</u> <u>Tissue</u>
    <u>Intl.</u> 1986, in press.
41. Leach, R.M.; Muenster, A.M. <u>J.</u> <u>Nutr.</u> 1962, <u>78</u>, 51–56.
42. Leach, R.M.; Muenster, A.M.; Wein, E. <u>Arch.</u> <u>Biochem.</u> <u>Biophys.</u>
    1969, <u>133</u>, 22–28.
43. Kagan, H.M. In <u>Biology</u> <u>of</u> <u>the</u> <u>Extra-cellular</u> <u>Matrix</u>;
    Mechan, R.P., Ed.; Academic Press: Fl, 1985; Vol. 1, p 1.

RECEIVED January 28, 1987

Chapter 6

Enhanced Tissue Lipid Peroxidation
Mechanism Underlying Pathologies Associated with Dietary Manganese Deficiency

Sheri Zidenberg-Cherr [1,2] and Carl L. Keen [1,3]

[1]Department of Nutrition, University of California—Davis, Davis, CA 95616
[2]Laboratory for Energy-Related Health Research, University of California—Davis, Davis, CA 95616
[3]Department of Internal Medicine, University of California—Davis, Davis, CA 95616

While it is recognized that a deficiency of Mn has pathological consequences, the underlying biochemical lesions have not been defined. One hypothesis is that Mn deficiency results in a reduction in Mn superoxide dismutase (MnSOD) activity with a subsequent increase in tissue lipid peroxidation and cellular damage. In support of this idea, Mn-deficient animals are characterized by low liver MnSOD activity and high levels of liver mitochondrial lipid peroxidation. Ultrastructural studies showing mitochondrial membrane abnormalities in liver from Mn-deficient rats support the hypothesis that increased tissue lipid peroxidation results in cellular damage. Based on the above it can be speculated that Mn deficiency should increase the cytotoxicity of environmental insults which increase the production of superoxide ion radical. Consistent with this idea is evidence that the metabolism of, and the physiological response to, a number of free radical inducers is affected by Mn status.

The essentiality of manganese (Mn) for animals was established in 1931 by Orent and McCollum (1) who reported that this element is required for normal reproduction in the rat, and Kemmerer and colleagues (2) who showed that it was necessary for normal growth and reproduction in the mouse. Since then several investigators have verified the critical need of this nutrient for normal development (3). Manifestations of perinatal Mn deficiency in experimental animals include neonatal death, impaired growth, skeletal abnormalities, depressed reproductive function, congenital ataxia, and defects in protein, carbohydrate and lipid metabolism. Although it is evident that Mn is needed for several biological functions, its precise biochemical roles have not been delineated.
Manganese is involved in numerous biochemical reactions both as an integral part of metalloenzymes and as an enzyme activator.

0097–6156/87/0354–0056$06.00/0
© 1987 American Chemical Society

Although there are numerous enzymes known to be activated by Mn, few Mn metalloenzymes have been recognized. With the exception of the glycosyl transferase enzymes, the enzymes for which Mn is a cofactor are usually non-specifically activated, with other divalent cations such as Mg^{++} being able to take the place of Mn^{++} (4,5).

Enzymes which contain Mn include pyruvate carboxylase, arginase, and superoxide dismutase. This paper will focus on the role of Mn as a component of Mn superoxide dismutase (MnSOD) and the functional significance of alterations in the activity of this enzyme.

Function of Manganese Superoxide Dismutase (MnSOD)

The majority of the O_2 reduced by aerobic cells is carried out through the 4 electron reductions by cytochrome oxidase (6), thus preventing the release of excessive amounts of reactive intermediates such as $O_2^{\cdot-}$, H_2O_2 and $\cdot OH$. However, small amounts of these reactive intermediates are generated during the reduction of O_2 to H_2O (7). In addition to the reduction of O_2 in the electron transport chain, the activity of a group of cellular enzymes which are involved in catalyzing oxidation reactions results in univalent reduction of O_2 to $O_2^{\cdot-}$. These include xanthine oxidase and peroxidases. As many of these enzymes are located in the mitochondria, these organelles can contribute substantial amounts of $O_2^{\cdot-}$. In addition, the autoxidation of a large group of compounds also contributes to the $O_2^{\cdot-}$ concentration in living systems. These include catecholamines, flavins and ferredoxin (8).

The O_2 flux in aerobic cells appears to have necessitated the development of SOD's which catalyze the dismutation of $O_2^{\cdot-}$ to H_2O_2 + O_2. Two types of SOD's have been described in mammalian cells. One contains Mn and is localized primarily in the mitochondria. The other contains Cu and Zn and is found primarily in the cytosol. Manganese superoxide dismutase isolated from chicken, rat and human liver has a molecular weight of 80,000 and contains 4 subunits of equal size, each containing one atom of Mn (9). In contrast to pyruvate carboxylase and arginase, the Mn in resting SOD is in the trivalent state. The catalytic cycle of this enzyme involves reduction and then reoxidation of the metal center during successive encounters with oxygen. Like other enzymes of the mitochondria which are synthesized in the cytoplasm, MnSOD is synthesized initially as a higher molecular weight precursor polypeptide. Final processing to the mature form presumably occurs in the mitochondria.

The high concentration of polyunsaturated fatty acids in cellular and subcellular membranes makes them particularly susceptible to free radical damage. In addition, mitochondrial membranes contain flavins as a part of their basic structure, potentially contributing $O_2^{\cdot-}$ resulting in free radical damage. The process of uncontrolled lipid peroxidation can result in the loss of essential polyunsaturated fatty acids, and the formation of toxic hydroperoxides and other secondary products. The loss of essential fatty acids may then result in loss of membrane integrity and loss of function. Extensive oxidation can also lead to rupture of subcellular membranes with subsequent release of lysosomal enzymes, and irreversible damage to the cell (10).

Influence of Dietary Manganese on MnSOD Activity

A dietary deficiency of Mn has been shown to result in a reduction of MnSOD activity in rats, mice, and chickens. In adult mice fed diets deficient in Mn (1 ug Mn/g diet) prenatally and postnatally, the activity of this enzyme was significantly lower in liver, brain, heart, and lung than in tissues of animals fed control diets (45 ug Mn/g diet) (11). In chickens, there was lower activity of MnSOD in liver after only 7 days of feeding a Mn-deficient diet (1 ug Mn/g diet) to hatchlings compared to controls. The activity of the enzyme was quickly elevated to normal by the feeding of Mn-adequate diets. Concomitant with the decline in activity of MnSOD, the activity of copper-zinc SOD (CuZnSOD) was increased, suggesting a compensatory response to $O_2^{\cdot-}$ which was not dismutated due to the lower MnSOD activity. Paynter (12) has reported that a reduction in heart and kidney MnSOD can also occur in rats when the deficient diets are initiated at weaning.

Functional Significance of Low MnSOD Activity

While the above shows that the activity of the enzyme can be affected by dietary Mn intake, it is important to determine if this reduction in activity is of physiological significance. An excellent model to study this question is the neonate. Birth and weaning are critical periods in the life of a mammal; both are associated with several pronounced enzyme changes. Immediately after birth, the neonate must depend on its glycogen reserves for a continuous supply of glucose. Later, gluconeogenic enzymes emerge, and the animal is capable of synthesizing glucose from glycolytic products and amino acids (13). There is an increase in oxidative metabolism during this period; thus an increase in the production of $O_2^{\cdot-}$ and increased activity of SOD might be expected, in order to combat its elevated production. Consistent with this idea are the findings by Yoshioka et al. (14) who reported that SOD activity was at its lowest level during the fetal period through day 5 of post-natal development in the rat. There was a rapid rise in activity from day 10 through day 20, reaching levels that were 88% of those observed in adults. Similar results were reported by Lankin and colleagues (15) and Mavelli et al. (16). If the Mn-deficient animal is unable to maintain an adequate level of enzymatic protection against oxygen-derived radicals, detrimental consequences may occur. For example, this may explain the high incidence of neonatal mortality observed in the Mn-deficient animal. To test this idea, we examined the changes that occur from birth to maturity (d 60) in the activity of MnSOD and CuZnSOD in several tissues of Mn-sufficient and -deficient mice.

In this study, tissue Mn concentrations increased with age in both groups; however, the imposition of a dietary Mn deficiency resulted in lower than normal levels of Mn by day 60 in all tissues examined. The developmental pattern of MnSOD activity paralleled that for Mn concentration (17).

Liver and kidney contained the greatest amount of MnSOD activity in mice, approximately 30% more than brain and heart. In the mature animal, Mn deficiency affected MnSOD activity most dramatically in the liver, with smaller changes in kidney and heart, and almost no change in the brain.

An intriguing observation is that MnSOD activity was retained even with the very low amounts of tissue Mn in deficient animals. These findings suggest the importance of enzymatic protection against free radical damage. It is interesting that normal levels of MnSOD were maintained in brains from Mn-deficient mice; we have limited data that indicate that Mn concentration is lower than normal in brains from Mn-deficient mice. Perhaps other roles of Mn in this tissue are being compromised in order to provide adequate MnSOD activity.

To assess the functional significance of lower than normal activity of MnSOD, we measured hepatic lipid peroxidation and MnSOD activity in Mn-sufficient and -deficient rats. In these studies we used rats in order to increase the amount of tissue available for the lipid peroxidation studies. Similar to the findings in mice, activity of liver MnSOD increased from birth through 60 days of age. By day 60, MnSOD activity in Mn-deficient rats was half that observed in Mn-sufficient rats (Figure 1). That this difference in SOD activity is of significance is suggested by the observation that at day 60, mitochondrial lipid peroxidation in Mn-deficient rats, as assessed by measuring TBA reacting products, was 3 times that observed in Mn-sufficient rats (Figure 2) (18). These findings suggested that the damage to mitochondrial membranes previously observed in Mn-deficient animals (1) was due in part to depressed MnSOD activity which resulted in increased lipid peroxidation from free radicals. To investigate this possibility the effects of Mn deficiency during prenatal and postnatal development on mitochondrial structure in the rat were assessed. Despite significant difference in MnSOD activity, livers from Mn-sufficient and -deficient rats from day 3 to day 60 exhibited normal ultrastructure (19). However, at 9 months of age, liver from three of the four Mn-deficient rats showed abnormal mitochondria, whereas those of control rats had normal ultrastructure. In the deficient animals, large vacuoles were present in the matrix of many mitochondria. The inner and outer mitochondrial membranes were separated from each other, creating open spaces. Similar abnormalities have been observed in liver from patients with Wilson's disease (20), diseases of mitochondrial myopathy (21), and Adriamycin treatment (22). The underlying mechanisms of these changes are unknown; however, excessive lipid peroxidation has been suggested as a contributing factor. We suggest that the mitochondrial abnormalities observed in the 9 month old Mn-deficient rats are at least in part the result of the lower MnSOD activity occurring at 60 days of age accompanied by excessive mitochondrial lipid peroxidation. Since no structural abnormalities were apparent earlier, the resulting mitochondrial damage observed in this study may have resulted from numerous factors contributing to structural damage over a period of time. For example, lipid composition of the membrane may have been altered due to elevated lipid peroxidation. Additionally, Mn is a cofactor for several enzymes functioning in

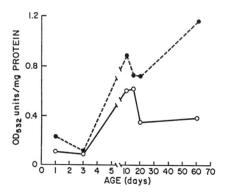

Figure 1. Age-related changes in rat liver MnSOD activity for
Mn-sufficient (——) and -deficient (- - -) rats. Values
shown are units/g liver wet weight. Each point represents the
mean of at least three rats.

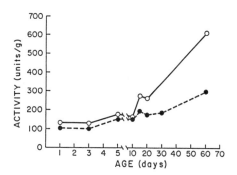

Figure 2. Lipid peroxidation as measured by TBA reacting
products (absorbance at 532 nm) in liver mitochondria for
Mn-sufficient (——) and -deficient (- - -) rats. Isolated
mitochondria were incubated in Tris-HCl buffer, pH 7.4, with the
addition of oxygen initiators. Each point represents the mean
of at least three rats.

cholesterol synthesis and fatty acid synthesis; thus alterations in
the synthesis of these compounds could contribute to abnormal
membranes (1).

Influence of Manganese Deficiency on Response to Free Radical Inducers

In addition to diet, the activity of MnSOD can be induced under
conditions which result in an increased production of $O_2^{\cdot-}$ such as
exposure to hyperbaric oxygen. Hyperoxia induces both MnSOD and
catalase activity in pulmonary macrophages whether the cells are
incubated in vitro or if the animals are exposed in vivo (23).
Similarly, ozone (O_3) inhalation has been shown to increase total
lung CuZnSOD and MnSOD activity in mice (24). Taken together these
findings suggest that an animal with an inadequate defense system
such as low MnSOD activity may be more susceptible to the deleter-
ious consequences of such agents. To assess the influence of Mn
status on the response to ozone exposure, Mn-sufficient and
-deficient mice were exposed to O_3 (1.21 ± 0.02 ppm) or filtered
air for 7 days (25). Regardless of dietary treatment, O_3 exposure
resulted in an increase in lung wet weight (Table I).

TABLE I.   Effect of Ozone Exposure on Mouse
Body and Lung Weight, and Lung SOD Activity

	Body wt (g)	Lung wt (g)	CuZnSOD (U/ g lung)	(U/ lung)	MnSOD (U/ g lung)	(U/ lung)
Mn-adequate						
Air	25.8±2.4	0.17±0.01	230±10	40±4	120±5	25±3
Ozone	26.7±0.86	0.22±0.02	190± 8	60±2	90±3	30±3
Mn-deficient						
Air	30.2±2.6	0.22±0.02	230±10	50±5	115±5	28±3
Ozone	31.1±1.7	0.35±0.02	220± 8	75±2	50±4	28±3

This increase reflects the edematous and inflammatory response of
the lung to O_3 exposure. Neither lung CuZnSOD nor MnSOD activity
was affected by diet in air-breathing groups. In marked contrast,
exposure to O_3 resulted in an increase in total lung SOD activity
in the Mn-sufficient group; this increase was a function of higher
activities of both MnSOD and CuZnSOD in these animals. Exposure to
O_3 also resulted in an increase in total SOD activity in Mn-
deficient mice; however, in these animals the increase occurred as
a result of a selective increase in CuZnSOD activity.

These results show that the typical increase in MnSOD activity
in response to O_3 exposure is impaired by dietary Mn deficiency.
The observation that there was a compensatory increase in the
activity of CuZnSOD in the Mn-deficient mice exposed to O_3 suggests
that the increase in the activities of this enzyme is in part
substrate-induced, and strongly supports the hypothesis that the
increase in lung SOD activity is an important response to O_3
exposure. Thus if the net increase in lung SOD activity is limited
by the nutritional status of the animal, then excessive lung damage
may occur due to free radical-initiated peroxidations.

Similar to O_3, alcohol is thought to exert some of its toxic effects through the production of $O_2^{\cdot -}$ during its metabolism. Consistent with this theory is the observation that alcohol feeding can result in increased SOD activity. In rats (26) and primates (27) ethanol consumption resulted in increased MnSOD activity.

In contrast to increased MnSOD activity, decreases in liver CuZnSOD activity were found with chronic ethanol feeding in rats and primates. Acute loads of ethanol feeding have also been reported to affect SOD levels. Mandal and co-workers (28) found that brain SOD levels were decreased in rats following acute ethanol feeding, and have suggested that some of the effects of ethanol on the nervous system are due to the cytotoxic effects of superoxide radicals. In contrast, Valenzuela and co-workers (29) reported an increase in liver SOD levels in rats given an acute feeding of ethanol. The difference between the results of Mandal and co-workers and Valenzuela and co-workers may be due to differences in the dietary status of their animals, tissue specificity, or the time sequence of the insults.

The above suggests that the increase in tissue MnSOD activity with ethanol consumption reflects a compensatory reaction to the increased $O_2^{\cdot -}$ load. Therefore the ability of the animal to increase the amount of this enzyme may dictate the extent of the pathology which could occur due to this insult. To test this hypothesis, Mn-sufficient and -deficient rats were given either 20% (w/v) ethanol or deionized water as their drinking fluid (30). There was no difference in daily caloric intake between the Mn-sufficient and -deficient rats not receiving ethanol. Both groups consumed approximately 15 g of purified diet a day, which is equivalent to about 68 kcal of metabolizable energy per day. From days 2-6, the daily caloric intake of the ethanol-fed rats decreased to 76 and 42% of that found in the rats not fed ethanol for Mn-sufficient and -deficient rats, respectively. Ethanol-fed rats were consuming 50% of their calories from ethanol and 50% from the diet. After day 6, the ethanol-fed Mn-sufficient rats increased their caloric intake above that of the rats not fed ethanol by eating more food and by drinking more ethanol than during the first 6 days. Their caloric intake during this period averaged 90 kcal/day, 50% from ethanol and 50% from diet. In contrast, the ethanol-fed Mn-deficient rats continued to consume an average of 30 kcal/day, 65% from ethanol and 35% from their food.

The body weight changes of the rats during this time were consistent with their caloric intake. During the first week of ethanol feeding, Mn-sufficient rats lost 15% of their initial body weight. However, during week 2 these rats gained an average of 9 g, which brought them to about 90% of their initial body weight. In contrast, the ethanol-fed Mn-deficient rats lost 20% of their initial body weight during week 1 and continued to lose weight during week 2. After 14 days of ethanol feeding, the ethanol-fed Mn-deficient rats were extremely lethargic and in poor condition, with pigment encrustation of the facial and neck region. After 14 days the body weight of this group of rats was only 65% of the initial weight. The consumption of ethanol by Mn-deficient rats resulted in a trend toward higher levels of liver Mn and liver MnSOD activity than those observed in deficient rats that were not

fed ethanol. However, these findings may be due to the fact that
liver size had decreased in this group. This finding is consistent
with those of Barak et al. (31) who observed that alcohol increases
the level of hepatic Mn in normal rats, and Dreosti et al. (26),
who reported an increase in cyanide-insensitive SOD activity after
ethanol consumption in normal rats.

Based on the lack of significant differences among the four
groups with regard to MnSOD activity it is unlikely that the
toxicity produced by ethanol in Mn-deficient rats was due simply to
inadequate levels of MnSOD, but rather represents an overall
diminished ability of the deficient animal to respond to this
particular agent.

Another agent which we have used to evaluate the influence of
Mn on superoxide metabolism is the antibiotic Adriamycin (ADR).
Adriamycin is considered one of the most potent drugs in the field
of chemotherapy, yet its clinical usefulness is compromised by a
number of serious side effects including a dose-dependent cardio-
toxicity. Adriamycin-induced heart disease is characterized by
degeneration of the cardiac muscle; mitochondria are enlarged and
the intracristal spaces are substantially extended.

We have evaluated the biochemical response of mice to ADR
treatment when fed either Mn-sufficient or -deficient diets. In
addition we varied the level of vitamin E to assess the influence
of a combined deficit of dietary antioxidants on ADR toxicity (33).

Adriamycin injection had no effect on liver Mn concentration.
In contrast, liver Fe concentration was influenced by both diet and
ADR injection. Although there was a trend towards higher than
normal concentrations of liver Fe in all groups treated with ADR,
only those animals fed diets low in both antioxidants had significantly higher levels (254.8 ± 72 ug Fe/g liver) than their saline-
injected controls (140.7 ± 44 ug Fe/g liver).

Heart MnSOD activity in the Mn-deficient mice was approximately 50% that of Mn-sufficient mice. Adriamycin injection had no
effect on heart MnSOD activity.

The TBA index was highest in those animals fed diets low in
vitamin E and Mn; values for this group were approximately 2-fold
higher than those observed in animals fed diets which were nutritionally complete. Adriamycin did not influence the TBA index in
any dietary group.

Results from this study showed that SOD activity was not
affected by acute ADR treatment. A second finding was that acute
ADR toxicity did not promote cardiac lipid peroxidation. However,
it was observed that mitochondrial lipid peroxidation was highest
in mice fed diets low in both antioxidants. Ultrastructural
examination revealed mitochondrial abnormalities in cardiac tissue
from ADR-treated animals (Figures 3 and 4). There were large
vacuoles within the mitochondria and condensation of the inner and
outer membranes of the mitochondria. The ultrastructural effects
of ADR treatment were most severe in the low E, Mn-deficient mice.
It is reasonable to suggest that a higher than normal level of
lipid peroxidation may predispose the animal to tissue damage from
ADR. Consistent with this concept, Meyers et al. (34) have
reported that pretreatment with supplemental vitamin E can reduce
the toxicity of ADR in mice.

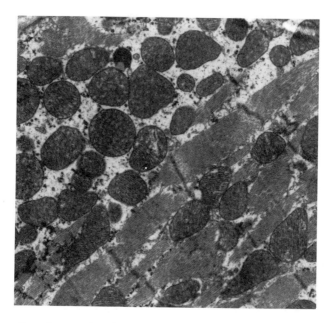

Figure 3. Heart mitochondria from a control mouse showing
normal ultrastructure (x 22,000).

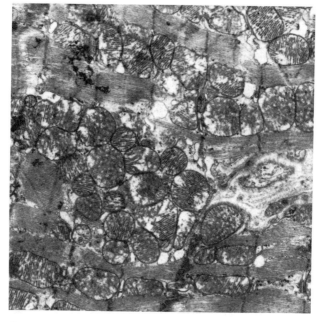

Figure 4. Heart mitochondria from an ADR-treated mouse fed a
diet low in vitamin E and Mn (x 22,000).

Summary

In the above it is evident that a consequence of Mn deficiency can be a profound reduction in MnSOD activity. Data from lipid peroxidation studies strongly support the concept that this reduction is of functional significance. In addition, the above findings demonstrate the fact that environmental insults and drugs which exert their toxic effects through the production of $O_2^{\cdot-}$ may exacerbate the effects of Mn deficiency. However, it is evident from the work on ozone and ADR that the response of Mn-deficient animals to free radical generators can vary. This suggests that the response to such insults may be tissue specific and/or dependent on the total amount of free radical generated.

Literature Cited

1. Orent, E. R.; McCollum, E. V. J. Biol. Chem. 1931, 92, 651-78.
2. Kemmerer, A. R.; Elvehjem, C. A.; Hart, E. B. J. Biol. Chem. 1931, 92, 623-30.
3. Keen, C. L.; Lonnerdal, B. In Manganese in Metabolism and Enzyme Function; Schramm, V. L. and Wedler, F. C., Eds.; Academic: Orlando, FL, 1986; pp 35-49.
4. Vallee, B. L.; Coleman, J. E. In Comprehensive Biochemistry; Florkin, M. and Stotz, E., Eds.; Elsevier: New York, 1964; Vol. 12, pp 165-235.
5. Leach, R. M., Jr. In Manganese in Metabolism and Enzyme Function; Schramm, V. L. and Wedler, F. C., Eds.; Academic: Orlando, FL, 1986; pp 81-92.
6. Antonini, E.; Brunori, M.; Greenwood, C.; Malmstrom, B. G. Nature 1970, 228, 936-7.
7. Clark, I. A. Pathology 1986, 18, 181-6.
8. Halliwell, B. Medical Biology 1984, 62, 71-7.
9. Beyer, W. F., Jr.; Fridovich, I. In Manganese in Metabolism and Enzyme Function; Schramm, V. L. and Wedler, F. C., Eds.; Academic: Orlando, FL, 1986; pp 193-217.
10. Tappel, A. L. In Free Radicals in Biology; Pryor, W., Ed.; Academic: New York, 1980; Vol. IV, pp 1-47.
11. deRosa, G.; Keen, C. L.; Leach, R. M.; Hurley, L. S. J. Nutr. 1980, 110, 795-804.
12. Paynter, D. L. J. Nutr. 1980, 110, 437-47.
13. Greengard, O. Assays Biochem. 1971, 7, 159-203.
14. Yoshioka, T.; Utsunio, K.; Sekiba, K. Biol. Neonate 1977, 32, 147-53.
15. Lankin, V. Z.; Tikhaze, A. K.; Lemeshko, V. V.; Shermatov, K.; Kaliman, L. A.; Vikhert, A. M. Byulleten Eksperimental noi Biologii i Meditsiny 1981, 92, 310-11.
16. Mavelli, I.; Rigo, A.; Federico, R.; Ciriolo, M.; Rotilio, G. Biochem. J. 1982, 204, 535-40.
17. Zidenberg-Cherr, S.; Keen, C. L.; Casey, S. M.; Hurley, L. S. Biol. Trace Element Res. 1985, 7, 209-19.
18. Zidenberg-Cherr, S.; Keen, C. L.; Lonnerdal, B.; Hurley, L. S. J. Nutr. 1983, 113, 2498-504.

19. Zidenberg-Cherr, S.; Keen, C. L.; Hurley, L. S. Biol. Trace Element Res. 1985, 7, 31-48.
20. Sternlieb, I. In Progress in Liver Disease; Popper, H. and Schaffner, F., Eds.; Grune and Stratton: New York, 1972; pp 511-525.
21. DiMauro, S.; Schotland, D. L.; Bonilla, E.; Lee, C. P.; Gambett, P.; Rowland, C. P. Arch. Neurol. 1973, 29, 170-9.
22. Pelikan, P. C.; Weisfeldt, M. L.; Jacobus, W. E.; Miceli, M. V.; Bulkley, B. H.; Gerstenblith, G. J. Cardiovascular Pharmacology 1986, 8, 1058-66.
23. Stevens, J. B.; Autor, A. P. Fed. Proc. 1980, 39, 3138-43.
24. Dubick, M. A.; Keen, C. L. Toxicol. Lett. 1983, 17, 355-60.
25. Dubick, M. A.; Zidenberg-Cherr, S.; Rucker, R. B.; Keen, C. L. Fed. Proc. 1987, 46, 912.
26. Dreosti, I. E.; Record, I. R.; Buckley, R. A.; Manuel, S. J.; Fraser, F. J. In Trace Element Metabolism in Man and Animals (TEMA-4); Howell, J. McC., Gawthorne, J. M. and White, C. L., Eds.; Griffin Press, Ltd.: Netley, South Australia, 1981; pp 617-620.
27. Keen, C. L.; Tamura, T.; Lonnerdal, B.; Hurley, L. S.; Halsted, C. H. Am. J. Clin. Nutr. 1982, 35, 836.
28. Mandal, P.; Ledig, M.; M'Paria, J. R. Pharmacol. Biochem. Behav. 1980, 13, 175-82.
29. Valenzuela, A.; Fernandez, N.; Fernandez, B.; Ugarte, G.; Vitela, L. A. FEBS Lett. 1980, 111, 11-13.
30. Zidenberg-Cherr, S.; Hurley, L. S.; Lonnerdal, B.; Keen, C. L. J. Nutr. 1985, 115, 460-7.
31. Barak, A. J.; Beckenhauer, H. C.; Kerrigan, F. J. Gut 1967, 8, 454-7.
32. Ogura, R.; Toyama, H.; Shimada, T.; Murakami, M. J. Appl. Biochem. 1979, 1, 325-35.
33. Zidenberg-Cherr, S.; Keen, C. L. Toxicol. Lett. 1986, 30, 79-87.
34. Myers, C. E.; McGuire, W. P.; Liss, R. H.; Ifrim, I.; Grotzinger, K.; Young, R. C. Science 1977, 197, 165-6.

RECEIVED August 20, 1987

Chapter 7

Iron in Manganese Metabolism

N. Gruden

Institute for Medical Research and Occupational Health, M. Pijade 158, 41001 Zagreb, Yugoslavia

The interaction of iron and manganese was studied on
intact white neonatal and weanling rats, and on the
everted intestinal segment of adult rats. The stim-
ulating effect of milk diet on manganese absorption
was eliminated by addition of iron to milk. This
inhibition of manganese absorption leveled off above
5 mg Fe/100 ml milk. It was observed after one day
of feeding on iron supplemented milk and disappeared
on the fourth day after withdrawing the supplementary
iron. Manganese retention in the intestinal wall was
far less affected by iron than its transport. The
competition between iron and manganese absorption is
is not yet developed in neonates but develops rather
abruptly in the third week of rat's life. To function
properly this competitive mechanism needs to be set
either by iron pretreatment or by a higher iron dose.

It has been recognized for a long time that there are a large
number of interactions among trace elements with possible profound
metabolic consequences (1,2). The knowledge about the physiological functions and optimum intake of trace elements should
therefore be considered in the light of interactions between them-
selves and with the other elements.

There are various mechanisms by which such interactions may
take place, like chemical association, competition for a binding
ligand-carrier, metabolic changes, membrane alteratios. The
result is usually that one elements inhibits the metabolic action
of another, but the two can also act sinergistically, causing a
effect greater than either element causes alone. The situation is
frequently rather complex, with an interactions between metals in a
chain of reactions (3). The subject has been appreciated by many
nutritionists. However, for different reasons, the knowledge
pertinent to humans has been developing rather slowly (4). Further
research may reveal that such interactions are of greater consequence to human health than it is now generally acknowledged.

We focus here our attention to the action of iron on manganese
metabolism, i.e. on the two most studied essential trace elements.

0097–6156/87/0354–0067$06.00/0

We shall also briefly touch upon the effect of iron on cadmium-manganese interaction.

The importance of manganese as an essential dietary component is well established. It is interesting to note that for 25 years after its essentiality was recognized, manganese has been treated as the trace element of purely academic importance. Nowadays it is a feed additive.

Manganese deficiency results in a wide variety of structural, physiological and biochemical defects, for it has been implicated in a number of metabolic and enzymatic processes (5-15). Hurley has summarized the evidence that manganese is essential for normal prenatal and neonatal development, with deficiency resulting in a variety of congenital malformations (16).

Manganese is also a toxic agent, though it can be regarded as one of the least toxic trace elements.   A wide margin of safety exists   between its intake which is essential for the organism and the concentrations associated with toxic effects (17).

Growth is rapid and many systems develop their adult cell number and composition throughout the first year of life. Optimal nutrition is thus most critical in this early period. Milk - the only source of food for the offspring of all mammals in the early months of life - cannot meet the demands of optimal growth later on in the first year of life. This is especially so with the essential elements such as iron and manganese whose low content in milk (18-23) does not meet the needs of a fast growing organism (24-27).

The effect of milk upon ions absorption from the intestinal tract has been studied extensively (28-33). The higher absorption of ions in the young than in the adult age (34-40) could be explained on the one hand by changes occuring in the intestinal membrane during the process of aging (41-45), or on the other hand, may be due to milk diet which is deprived of several essential elements (28-33). Yet milk diet does not affect the metabolism of all ions equally. For instance, a seven-day-long milk diet which neither alters the transport of calcium nor of lead in six-week-old female albino rats (46), significantly increases the manganese transport and retention in the duodenum of these animals (47). The latter effect could be explained neatly by the low manganese content of milk (48-52) were it not that milk fortification by manganese enhanced even further, highly significantly, the manganese transfer and intestinal retention (47). Thus it seems fairly conclusive that it is not manganese deficiency in milk which is responsible for an overall enhancement of manganese transfer into and through the duodenal wall in milk-treated animals.

There is a possibility that some milk constituents regulate the absorption of ions in the intestine. In studying manganese metabolism we turned to the low iron content in milk. Iron has received great attention in pediatric nutrition. The concern has been to prevent the anemia caused by iron deficiency earlier often found in childhood. Wide milk consumption by infants and young children makes this   food   an attractive vehicle for iron fortification. Iron-enriched proprietary milk substitutes can adequately prevent the anemia common to infants who subsist largely on low-iron mother's or cow's milk (53).

Yet, there is insufficient knowledge about the biological availability of this element, and the optimal levels have not yet

been adequately determined. There is a risk of too high a level
with putatively diverse effects of increasing the dietary iron
content (54-59). Further, since the amount of iron in the diet and
the iron body state influence the absorption of some essential and
non-essential elements (60-71), the interaction between the minerals
thay may have harmful effects on the body is always possible. In
view of all this we considered it worthwhile to study the effect of
iron upon manganese metabolism, following thus the line initiated
by some authors years ago (72-74).

All our experiments were performed on rats. Although "man is
not a big rat" (75) and extrapolation of experimental findings from
animals to humans is generally difficult, according to Mahoney and
Hendricks (76) rats and humans respond qualitatively similarly to
many dietary and physiological factors known to influence iron
utilization. These authors have found iron absorption by rats to be
highly correlated with that in humans - a rather important finding
for our (iron-manganese interactions) studies performed on rats.

Studies In Vitro

The experimental animals were female albino rats, mostly five weeks
old. Iron-manganese interaction was studied on the everted duodenal segment (77) where the transport and absorption of the two
metals per unit of time are higher than in the more distal parts of
the intestine (78-82). Manganese-54 and iron-59 were used as
markers for their stable isotopes.

Manganese Transport. Our first experiments showed that when milk
was enriched with iron in doses which equalized the daily amount of
iron received with milk to that of the stock diet (10 mg Fe/100 ml),
the transduodenal transport of manganese became equal for animals
fed on these two different diets (47). In other words, the stimu-
lative effect of the original, iron-deficient milk upon manganese
transport disappeared completely, confirming thus the competition
of iron and manganese at the expense of the latter (72-74). It
comes to one's mind, of course, that the tissue deprived of manganese through a milk diet will utilize more of the offered manganese.
However, experiments with rats fed manganese-enriched milk resulted
in more than a doubled transfer of manganese-54 (47), showing thus
that it is not the manganese deficiency in milk which is responsible
for the enhanced manganese-54 transfer in milk-fed animals. Moreover, when both manganese and iron content of milk were raised to
the level in the stock diet, the inhibitory effects of iron upon
manganese was still dominant (47).

All this indicates that there are some transport mechanisms
common to iron and manganese so that in the presence of both ions
manganese will be discriminated in favor of iron. These findings
suggest also that the pretreatment in vivo with plain or enriched
milk diet induces permeability changes in the duodenal wall which
persist at least long enough for the manganese transport to be
accomplished in vitro.

Dose Dependency. When the animals were fed only cow's milk fortified with different doses of ferrous sulphate (0.60-19.0 mg Fe/100
ml) for three days before killing, manganese transfer and its

duodenal retention alike followed the iron-dose dependency suggest-
ive of a saturation effect (83). The inhibition had a mildly expressed maximum around 2.5 mg Fe/100 ml milk with a leveling of
above 5 mg Fe/100 ml milk. The simplest and most plausible
rationalization of this effect was (again) that there is a competitive relationship between iron and manganese for the carrier so
that iron is the preferred ion with a probably higher affinity for
the binding sites within the mucosa.

To what extent the mechanism regulating manganese absorption
is dependent on the amount of iron in the diet is shown also by the
following. Even at a ten-fold increase in dietary manganese (from
5.6 to 56.0 mg Mn/100 g food), at two concentrations of dietary
iron (13 and 59 mg Fe/100 g food), changes in the duodenal transport of manganese were only marginally significant (84). On the
contrary, for the animals fed plain iron deficient milk the results
showed a marked dependence on manganese consumption, i.e. by
increasing manganese concentration in milk (from 0.9 to 9.6 mg/100
ml), transduodenal transfer of manganese also increased. Similarly,
the addition of manganese from 1.4 to 10.0 mg/100 ml to milk containing 5 or 20 mg of iron in 100 ml slightly reduced or left
unchanged the transfer of radiomanganese through the duodenal wall
(85). When the same amount of manganese was added to milk which
had not been enriched with iron, manganese transfer significantly
increased (47).

A possible reason why manganese addition to milk and stock
diets gives different results may well be a differences in iron
content between the two diets. In the case of an iron deficient
diet (milk), the (regulation of) manganese absorption is set only
by the manganese level of the diet. With 5 and 20 mg Fe/100 ml the
iron content is within its saturation ("plateau") level (83). It
thus influences manganese metabolism similarly to the stock diet.
Obviously, by increasing the iron level in milk above a threshold
(2.5 mg/100 mg, 83) the transfer and intestinal retention of manganese become independent of both the iron and manganese levels.

Time Dependence. As the initial iron deficiency (by milk feeding)
stimulates iron absorption (53,86-90), which in turn may affect
negatively manganese absorption (as described here), the body iron
state must also be taken into account. It is therefore useful to
establish data about the time factor, i.e. how long the animals can
be treated with iron supplemented milk before an alteration in manganese transport is observed and also, how long it takes for manganese transport to return to normal once iron treatment has ceased.
The relevant experiments showed that the inhibition of manganese
transfer was present after one day of feeding on iron supplemented
(10 mg Fe/100 ml) milk. The inhibition leveled off already after
the second day of such feeding. The reverse effect – on withdrawing
the supplementary iron (i.e. 0.05 mg Fe/100 ml in pure milk) – was
much slower, the increase in manganese transport having become
noticeable after the fourth day (91).

The fact that the onset of inhibition of manganese transport
and retention by iron is faster than its disappearance may also be
due to a higher affinity of the carrier binding sites for iron than
for manganese. Once filled up with iron these sites will resist
iron deficiency for a longer time than they would need to get

loaded with iron after an iron deficient state. As both the appearance and disappearance of the inhibitory effect of iron takes days, it is likely that the intestinal wall undergoes some reversible changes.

Iron absorption is regulated by the cells of the intestinal mucosa according to the body's need (68,87-89,90,92). In iron deficiency the epithelial iron content is reduced and its uptake as well as transfer to the blood increased, while in the loaded state the situation is opposite. Owing to the chemical similarity of iron and manganese it is reasonable to assume that the iron binding material in the intestinal mucosal cells can also bind manganese, especially in the iron deficient state. After three days of feeding with an iron-poor milk, iron deposits in the intestinal wall are mostly used up by the body. As the binding sites involved in the transfer of metals from the mucosa to the serosa show a greater affinity for iron than for manganese, the latter can replace iron only in the iron deficient state.

On the whole, manganese retention in the intestinal wall is far less affected by iron than its transport (47,91), which suggests that the binding sites for manganese (or iron) transport are not the same as for their retention in the mucosa. In other wards, the transport binding sites are more sensitive to iron deficiency. Nothing, of course, can be said about actual molecular differences between the two types of binding sites.

The effect of iron upon manganese transfer was shown to be significantly higher in the duodenum than in the jejunum or ileum. As for animals' age and sex it was observed that iron effect upon manganese transfer and intestinal retention was more pronounced in the young (6-week-old) than in the old rats (16- and 26-week old), and in female than in male rats. Surprisingly, the effect was more dependent on sex than on animals' age (Gruden, N., unpublished data).

Iron Transport. To gain additional insight into the iron-manganese interaction, the experiments were performed in which the influence of milk, either pure or fortified with iron and/or manganese, on iron transduodenal transport was studied (93). The results corroborated our former interpretation. Namely, compared with the standard diet as control, a three-day feeding with cow's milk alone resulted in a two and a half times higher total transduodenal radioiron transport. The stimulatory effect of milk was the same if manganese was added to milk (1.1 mg Mn/100 ml), but disappeared completely after the addition of 10 mg Fe/100 ml, alone or together with 1.1 mg manganese/100 ml milk.

Simultaneously, there was no significant change in radioiron uptake in the intestinal wall. This confirms the assumption that the binding sites for iron (and manganese) transport are not the same as for their retention in the mucosa. These processes could be regarded as independent so that changes in one need not necessarily be accompanied by changes in the other (73,74).

Under identical experimental conditions iron deficiency definately stimulates much more the transduodenal transport and intestinal uptake of radiomanganese than of radioiron (47,93). This could be explained by the much more stable absorption and other mechanisms in the intestine for iron than for manganese. Whereas the homeostasis of iron is maintained at the level of the intestinal

tract (68,86,87,89,90,92), manganese homeostasis is regulated (also)
at the excretion level no matter how much manganese has been absorbed
from the intestine (8,94-97).

The fact that manganese had no effect on iron transport could be
explained by different K_m values for iron and manganese (73). This
again suggests that the shared intestinal transport system shows less
affinity for manganese than for iron and explains a greater inhibitory effect of iron on manganese absorption than of manganese on
iron absorption. It may also be that there exists iron-binding sites
which if free from iron could be used to manganese transport and that
other manganese-binding sites are present in much greater abundance
but are used exclusively for manganese ions. The latter conclusion,
reached also for Forth and Rummel (98) is strongly supported by the
fact that the enrichment of iron-poor milk with manganese enhances
the transfer and intestinal retention of radiomanganese but does
not affect iron transport (93).

Two conclusions which could have practical importance may be
derived so far: 1) in combating neonatal iron deficiency, by
increasing simultaneously iron and manganese content in milk it
might be possible to diminish the risk of manganese deficiency and
2) milk does not seem to be the best means of additional nutrition
in exposure to manganese.

Studies In Vivo

In view of literature data and our (in vitro) results on iron-
manganese interaction, we considered it worthwhile to study the effect
of iron on manganese metabolism in very young rats when absorptive,
homeostatic and competitive mechanisms in the intestinal tract are
not yet functioning properly or are in a developing phase. We performed experiments to see what role iron dose, duration of treatment
and animals' age have in iron-manganese competition at an early
period of rat's life.

Five- to 21-day-old white rats were used. The animals were
placed into groups according to the amount of iron they had received
in iron supplemented cow's milk for either one ("non-pretreated") or
four days ("pretreated"). Iron doses were from 52 to 1000 µg Fe/ml
milk. Radioisotopes (Mn-54 or Fe-59) were always administered by
the artificial "drop-by-drop" feeding procedure (99). The radioactivity was determined in selected organs (liver, kidney, spleen,
brain, femure, intestinal tract, stomach) in addition to measurements
of the whole body and carcass.

Sucklings. Although the inhibitory effect of iron on manganese
absorption is recognized (2,47,72-74,83,91,100), it is not known when
precisely it sets in. It seems that in the neonatal, six-day-old
rats the competition between iron and manganese absorption is not yet
developed. Namely, the addition for one (101) or four days (102) of
low, physiological amounts of iron to milk diet (50 or 100 µg Fe/ml)
did not appreciably decrease manganese absorption. Moreover, in
neonatal rats treated with these iron doses for four days, manganese-
54 values in the whole body (absorption), intestine, liver and
kidneys were even greater by 10 to 52 percent than in the controls
receiving plain cow's milk (102). No interpretation can be offered
why and how the introduction of low iron doses increased

radiomanganese absorption at the same dietary manganese level for
all animal groups.

However, when a dose of 200 µg Fe/ml or higher (410-1000 µg Fe/
ml) was administered even on a single day, it caused in these six-
day-old rats a significant and mainly dose-dependent diminution of
manganese absorption and organ uptake, with the exception of the
liver (103). Our explanation is that a) at that early age the lower
iron doses (below 200 µg Fe/ml) have no effect whatsoever on the
route(s) of manganese transport and b) that owing to lack of homeostatic iron regulation at that age (104) the large(r) amounts of
iron introduced (doses of 200, 410 and 1000 µg Fe/ml) can block the
manganese pathways. The latter conclusion is corroborated by the
enhanced iron retention (104) and the diminished manganese one in
the liver and intestine (103). In other words, in the absence of a
regulatory mechanism for iron absorption, its enhanced uptake owing
to high amounts of iron added to the milk diet eliminates manganese.
This in turn implies that the organism at such an early age is much
more prone to accept iron at the expense of manganese.

Weanlings. In three-week-old rats   i.e., at an age when some histobiochemical changes take place in the intestinal tract (41,42,45,105,
106) the effect of iron on manganese metabolism is somewhat different
from that in neonatal animals. According to some authors (107) the
iron content of the weanling diet plays even a critical role in
terminal maturation of rat small intestine. Anyhow, doses of 100 and
200 µg Fe/ml, administered on a single day enhanced significantly
(by 30-40 percent) radiomanganese absorption in weanling rats, thus
influencing also manganese distribution within their organism. At
higher iron concentrations (410 and 1000 µg Fe/ml), a significant
drop (25-35 percent with respect to the controls fed with no additional iron in milk) in manganese absorption was observed (103). It
thus appears that in the weaning age manganese does not have to compete with iron if iron doses can be controlled by the homeostatic
mechanism. However, with the dose of 410 µg Fe/ml iron-manganese
competition sets in abruptly, as (probably) the still large absolute
amounts of iron block the manganese pathways to an appreciable
degree.

It must be emphasized that the homeostatic regulation of iron
absorption is efficient in weaning but not in neonatal rats (104).
In consequence, large amounts of iron prevent manganese transport in
neonatals. The same is true of the weanlings but at the higher iron
doses, when the homeostatic iron regulation cannot suppress iron
amounts below the threshold causing competition with manganese. It
turns out that the dose of 410 µg Fe/ml milk is above the threshold
irrespective of whether it is applied during a four-day treatment
(4 x 100 µg Fe/ml, 108), or given on a single day (103).

It is concluded that the mechanisms which regulate iron-
manganese competition, although operating in the intestine of weanling rats, in order to function properly need to be activated either
by iron doses above a certain threshold (103) or by some duration
(four days - in our case, 108) of treatment with lower iron doses.

The Development of Iron-Manganese Competition. The competitive
effect of iron upon manganese absorption depends not only on the
duration of iron treatment (101,102,108) and on the iron dose

administered (103), but also, to a great extent on the animals age
(108). The question remains whether this effect is triggered off
abruptly in the rat's weaning age, or whether it is developing grad-
ually from the neonatal till the weaning period.

Experiments performed on 8,11,14 and 17-day-old animals together
with the earlier results on five-day- (102) and three-week-old rats
(108) indicate that manganese absorption does not significantly
differ between the control (plain milk diet) and iron-treated rats
(100 μg Fe/ml diet-during four days) until the 17th day of age.
From then on it sharply decreases in the iron-pretreated animals to
attain in the third week as much as 50 percent lower values than in
control animals (109). The abrupt diminution of manganese retention
(as well as that of iron-59 in identical experiments, (110) in iron-
pretreated animals between the 17th and 21st day of life is likely
to be due to the alterations taking place in the intestinal tract of
the rat at that age. Having in mind that that is also the time of
weaning, one is impelled to take into account the type of food consumed by the animals. However, our weanling rats switched over from
mother's to cow's milk and not to the standard laboratory food.
Thus, any major effect due to a change of food consistency can be
eliminated. In all likelihood it is the histobiochemical change in
the intestine that facilitates the onset of iron-manganese interaction within this brief period of life.

Summarizing, it may be concluded that the mechanisms regulating
iron-manganese interaction become operative in the third week of
the rat's life, i.e., at the same time when the regulation of iron
absorption is fully activated. Experimental evidence suggests that
the onset of this regulation is not provoked by a change from milk
to solid food.

Iron and Cadmium-Manganese Interactions

The effect of iron on cadmium-manganese interaction will be briefly
dealt with. The data about the effect of cadmium on manganese
metabolism are rather scanty (78,111-114). Nevertheless, some data
clearly show that manganese transfer through and its retention in
the rat's duodenal wall are significantly depressed in the presence
of cadmium (115). By the simultaneous addition of iron to the
animals' milk diet the action of iron and cadmium upon manganese
absorption becomes synergistic. This is substantiated by the observation that the already existing inhibitory effect of cadmium is
enhanced by 10 to 60 percent in the presence of iron and, in addition, that it becomes noticeable even at such low doses of cadmium
at which otherwise there is none (Gruden, N., Proc. 5th Int. Symp.
Trace Elem., Jena 1986, in press).

A saturation effect is indicated in that iron enhances iden-
tically the cadmium inhibitory effect upon manganese absorption
irrespective of the cadmium dose. In addition, the iron dose does
not alter only the already strong effect of high cadmium dose.
Furthermore, within a span of 5.0-15.0 mg Fe/100 ml iron has an
equal effect upon cadmium action, while below 2.5 mg Fe/100 ml it
does not alter the effect of cadmium at all. This is yet another
indication of iron saturation at a level above 5.0 mg Fe/ml milk,
as observed earlier (83).

A plausible rationalization would be that there is a competition for the transport route through the intestinal wall between cadmium and manganese on the one side, and between iron and manganese on the other. The competition, i.e., absorption in the intestinal tract, depends upon the relative concentration of these ions and kinetics of and affinity for their interaction with the binding sites in the intestinal mucosa.

Concluding Remarks

During the past fifteen to twenty years observations have accumulated to an extent which enables us to grasp the framework of a complex relationship between two essential elements, iron and manganese.

The competition between the two for the transport through the intestinal wall, i.e., absorption and their retention within the various organs must be viewed with regard to the evolving overall homeostatic mechanism on the one hand, and the histobiochemical alterations of the tissues on the other. It has thus been established that the iron-manganese competition in the intestine at the expense of manganese sets in rather suddenly between the 17th and 21st day of the rats life. The reversal of iron-manganese effects in neonatal to those in weanlings is not due to the change from liquid (milk) to solid food, but (most probably) to the full activation of the mechanism regulating iron absorption. The competition is evident with iron doses that can be controlled by the homeostatic mechanism, but the difference in the homeostatic sites for iron and manganese must be taken into account in rationalizing their interplay.

The pretreatment in vivo with plain or enriched milk diet induces changes in the permeability of the intestinal wall which persist at least long enough for manganese transport to be accomplished in vitro. There is obviously a competitive relationship between iron and manganese for the carrier so that iron is the preferred ion with a probably higher affinity for the binding sites within the mucosa. This also explains the fact that the inhibition of manganese transport and retention evolves faster on iron application, than it disappears after iron withdrawal. As both the appearance and disappearance of the inhibitory effect of iron take days, it is likely that the intestinal wall undergoes some reversible changes.

Manganese retention in the intestinal wall is far less affected by iron than its transport, which suggests that the binding sites for manganese (or iron) transport are not the same as for their retention in the intestinal mucosa. In other words, the transport binding sites are more sensitive to iron deficiency, which means that iron deficiency stimulates much more the transduodenal transport of manganese (and iron) than their intestinal uptake.

From the practical standpoint of particular importance is that it is not the manganese deficiency in milk that is responsible for an overall enhancement of manganese transfer into and through the duodenal wall in milk-treated animals. It is rather the availability to manganese of the iron-carrier sites owing to the low iron content of milk. Hence, milk does not seem to be the best means of additional nutrition in exposure to manganese. On the other hand, it might be possible to diminish the risk of manganese deficiency in combating neonatal iron deficiency by increasing simultaneously iron and manganese content in milk.

In the future research will have to be engaged in explaining at the molecular level why iron inhibits manganese transfer and absorption in the intestinal tract.

Literature Cited

1. Sandstead, H.H. J. Lab. Clin. Med. 1981, 98, 457.
2. Mills, C.F. Ann. Rev. Nutr. 1985, 5, 1973.
3. Magos, L.; Webb, M. Environ. Health Perspect. 1978, 25, 151.
4. Burch, R.E.; Sullivan, J.F. Med. Clin. North Am. 1976, 60, 655.
5. Hurley, L.S.; Theriault-Bell, L. J. Nutr. 1974, 104, 133.
6. Utter, M.F. Med. Clin. North Am. 1976, 60, 713.
7. Theriault-Bell, L.; Hurley, L.S. Proc. Soc. Exp. Biol. Med. 1974, 145, 1321.
8. Hidiroglou, M. Can. J. Ani. Sci. 1979, 59, 217.
9. Khandelwal, S.; Kachru, D.N.; Tandon, S.K. Environ. Res. 1981, 24, 75.
10. Amesz, J. Biochim. Biophys. Acta 1983, 726, 1.
11. Keen, C.L.; Baly, D.L.; Lonnerdal, B. Biol. Trace Elem. Res. 1984, 6, 309.
12. Donaldson, J. Neurotoxicology 1984, 5, 1.
13. Erikson, H.; Morath, C.; Heilbronn, E. Neurol. Scand. 1984, 70, 89.
14. Baly, D.L.; Curry, D.L.; Keen, C.L.; Hurley, L.S. Endocrinology 1985, 116, 1734.
15. Zidenberg-Cherr, S.; Keen, C.L.; Hurley, L.S. Biol. Trace. Element Res. 1985, 7 31.
16. Hurley, L.S. Physiol. Rev. 1981, 61, 249.
17. Cooper, W.C. J. Toxicol. Environ. Health. 1984, 14, 23.
18. Vouri, E. Acta Paediatr. Scand. 1979, 68, 571.
19. Lonnerdal, B.; Keen, C.L.; Hurley, L.S. Ann. Rev. Nutr. 1981, 1, 149.
20. Kosta, L.; Byrne, A.R.; Dermelj, M. Sci. Total Environ. 1983, 29, 261.
21. Stastny, D.; Vogel, R.S.; Picciano, M.R. Am. J. Clin. Nutr. 1984, 39, 872.
22. Casey, C.E.; Hambidge, K.M.; Neville, M.C. Am. J. Clin. Nutr. 1985, 41, 1193.
23. Gunshin, H.; Yoshikawa, M.; Doudou, T.; Kato, N. Agric. Biol. Chem. 1985, 49, 21.
24. Vuori, E. Br. J. Nutr. 1979, 42, 407.
25. Oski, F.A.; Stockman, J.A. Pediatr. Clin. North Am. 1980, 27, 237.
26. Beaton, G.H. Pediatr. Clin. North Am. 1985, 32, 275.
27. Oski, F.A. Pediatr. Clin. North Am. 1985, 32, 493.
28. Kello, D.; Kostial, K. Environ. Res. 1973, 6, 355.
29. Stephens, R.; Waldron, H.A. J. Toxicol. 1975, 13, 555.
30. Engstrom, B.; Nordberg, G. Toxicology 1978, 9, 195.
31. Moore, M.R. Proc. Nutr. Soc. 1979, 38, 243.
32. Bell, R.R.; Spickett, J.T. Fd. Cosmet. Toxicol. 1981, 19, 429.

33. Quarterman, J.; Morrison, E. Proc. Nutr. Soc. 1981, 40, 25A.
34. Shiraishi, Y.; Ichikawa, R. Health Phys. 1972, 22, 373.
35. Jugo, S. Environ. Res. 1977, 13, 36.
36. Kostial, K.; Simonovic, I.; Raber, I.; Blanusa, M.; Landeka, M. Environ. Res. 1983, 31, 111.
37. Kostial, K. In Health Evaluation of Heavy Metals in Infant Formula and Junior Food; Schmidt, E.H.F.; Hildebrandt, A.G., Eds., Springer Verlag: Berlin Heidelberg, 1983, p. 99.
38. Kostial, K. Environ. Health Perspect. 1984, 54, 51.
39. Kirchgessner, M.; Weigan, E.; Schwarz, F.J. In TEMA-4; Howell, J.McC.; Gawthorne, J.M.; White, C.L. Eds., Australian Academy of Science: Canberra, 1981, p. 125.
40. Hassan Raghib, M.; Chan, W.Y.; Rennert, O.M. Nutr. Rep. Int. 1985, 32, 1201.
41. Hohn, P., Schafer, A., Gabbert, H. Mechan. Aging Develop. 1977, 6, 35.
42. Henning, S. Am. J. Physiol. 1981, 241, G199.
43. Kwo-Yih, Y. J. Nutr. 1983, 113, 1496.
44. Koldowsky, O. J. Am. Coll. Nutr. 1984, 3, 131.
45. Udall, J.N.; Bloch, K.J.; Vachino, G.; Feldman, P.; Walker, W.A. Biol. Neonate 1984, 45, 289.
46. Gruden, N. Ingoslav. Physiol. Pharmacol. Acta 1976, 12, 47.
47. Gruden, N. Nutr. Reports Int. 1976, 14, 515.
48. Watson, L.T.; Ammerman, C.B.; Feaster, J.P.; Roessler, C.E. J. Ani. Sci. 1973, 36, 131.
49. Carter, J.C., Jr.; Miller, W.J.; Neathery, M.W.; Gentry, R.P.; Stake, P.E.; Blackmon, D.M. J. Ani. Sci. 1974, 38, 1284.
50. Abrams, E.; Lassiter, J.W.; Miller, W.J.; Neathery, M.W.; Gentry, R.P. Nutr. Rep. Int. 1976, 14, 561.
51. Abrams, E.; Lassiter, J.W.; Miller, W.J.; Neathery, M.W.; Gentry, R.P.; Scarth, R.D. J. Ani. Sci. 1976, 42, 630.
52. Craig, W. Nutr. Rep. Int. 1984, 30, 1003.
53. Finch, C.A.; Cook, J.D. Am. J. Clin. Nutr. 1984, 39, 471.
54. Chandra, R.K. Immunology Today 1983, 4, 322.
55. Abe, F.; Tateyma, M.; Shibuya, H.; Azumi, N.; Ommura, Y. Mycopathologia 1985, 89, 59.
56. Barclay, R. Med. Lab. Sci. 1985, 42, 166.
57. Letendre, E.D. Trends Biochem. Sci. 1985, 10, 166.
58. Mevissen-Verhage, E.A.E.; Marcelis, J.H.; Harmsen-van Amerogen, W.C.M.; de Vos, N.M.; Berkel, J.; Verhoef, J. Eur. J. Clin. Microbiol. 1985, 4, 14.
59. Ward, C.G. Am. J. Surg. 1986, 151, 291.
60. Solomons, N.W.; Jacob, R.A. Am. J. Clin. Nutr. 1981, 34, 475.
61. Valberg, L.S.; Flanagan, P.R.; Chamberlain, M.J. Am. J. Clin. Nutr. 1984, 40, 536.
62. Shimoda, M.; Yawata, Y. Am. J. Haematol. 1985, 19, 55.
63. Hamilton, D.L. Toxicol. Appl. Pharmacol. 1978, 46, 651.
64. Flanagan, P.R.; Hamilton, D.L.; Haist, J.; Valberg, L.S. Gastroenterology 1979, 77, 1074.
65. Carpenter, S.J. Toxicology 1982, 24, 259.
66. Ragan, H.A. Proc. Soc. Exp. Biol. Med. 1975, 150, 36.
67. Flanagan, P.R.; McLellan, J.S.; Haist, J.; Cherian, G.; Chamberlain, M.J.; Valberg, L.S. Gastroenterology 1978, 74, 841.

68. Ragan, H.A. Sci. Total Environ. 1983, 28, 317.
69. Leon, L.; Johnson, D.R. J. Toxicol. Environ. Health 1985, 15, 687.
70. Becker, G.; Huebers, H.; Rummel, W. Blut 1979, 38, 397.
71. Sephton, R.; Martin, J.J. Br. J. Radiol. 1980, 53, 572.
72. Pollack, S.; George, J.N.; Reba, R.C.; Kaufman, R.M.; Crosby, W.H. J. Clin. Invest. 1965, 44, 1470.
73. Thomson, A.B.R.; Olatunbosun, D.; Valberg, L.S.; Ludwig, J. J. Lab. Clin. Med. 1971, 78, 642.
74. Thomson, A.B.R.; Valberg, L.S. Am. J. Physiol. 1972, 223, 1327.
75. Oser, B.L. J. Toxicol. Environ. Health 1981, 8, 521.
76. Mahoney, A.W.; Hendrics, D.G. Nutr. Res. 1984, 4, 913.
77. Wilson, T.H.; Wiseman, G. J. Physiol. (Lond.) 1954, 123, 116.
78. Sahagian, B.M.; Harding-Barlow, I.; Perry, H.M. Jr. J. Nutr. 1966, 90, 259.
79. Ansari, M.S.; Miller, W.J.; Neathery, M.W.; Lassiter, J.W.; Gentry, R.P. Nutr. Reports Int. 1977, 15, 37.
80. Howard, J.; Jacobs, A. Brit. J. Haematol. 1977, 23, 595.
81. Gruden, N.; Buben, M. Iugoslav. Physiol. Pharmacol. Acta 1978, 14, 83.
82. Richter, G.W.; Lee, Y.H. Experientia 1982, 38, 583.
83. Gruden, N. Nutr. Metab. 1977, 21, 305.
84. Gruden, N. Period. Biol. 1979, 81, 567.
85. Gruden, N.; Buben, M. Period. Biol. 1980, 82, 9.
86. Charlton, R.W.; Jacobs, P.; Torrance, J.D.; Bothwell, T.H. J. Clin. Invest. 1965, 44, 543.
87. Narasinga Rao, B.S. Br. Med. Bull. 1981, 37, 25.
88. Huebers, H.; Finsh, C.A. Semin. Hematol. 1982, 19, 3.
89. Refsum, S.B.; Schreiner, B.B. Scand. J. Gastroenterol. 1984, 19, 867.
90. Nathanson, M.H.; Muir, A.; McLaren, G.D. Am. J. Physiol. 1985, 245, G439.
91. Gruden, N. Nutr. Reports Int. 1977, 15, 577.
92. Finch, C.A.; Huebers, H.A. Clin. Physiol. Biochem. 1986, 4, 5.
93. Gruden, N. Nutr. Reports Int. 1979, 19, 69.
94. Miller, W.J. Fed. Proc. 1973, 32, 1915.
95. Klaassen, C.D. Toxicol. Appl. Pharmacol. 1974, 29, 458.
96. Kojima, S.; Hirai, M.; Kiyozumi, M.; Sasawa, Y.; Nakagawa, M.; Shin-o, T. Chem. Pharm. Bull. 1983, 31, 2459.
97. Symonds, H.W.; Hall, E.D. Res. Veter. Sci. 1983, 33, 5.
98. Forth, W.; Rummel, W. Physiol. Rev. 1973, 53, 724.
99. Kostial, K.; Simonovic, I.; Pisonic, M. Nature (London) 1967, 215, 1181.
100. Khandelwal, S.; Asquin, M.; Tandon, S.K. Bull. Environ. Contam. Toxicol. 1984, 32, 10.
101. Gruden, N. Reprod. Nutr. Develop. 1980, 20, 1539.
102. Gruden, N.; Buben, M. Nutr. Reports Int. 1981, 24, 943.
103. Gruden, N. Nutr. Reports Int. 1986,
104. Gruden, N. Nutr. Reports Int. 1986, 33, 693.
105. Baintner, K., Jr.; Veress, B. Experientia 1970, 26, 54.
106. Forbes, G.B.; Reina, J.C. J. Nutr. 1972, 102, 647.
107. Buts, J.P.; Delacroix, D.L.; Dekeyser, N.; Paquet, S.; Horsman, Y.; Boelens, M.; et al. Am. J. Physiol. 1984, 246, G745.

108. Gruden, N. Nutr. Reports Int. 1982, 25, 849.
109. Gruden, N. Nutr. Reports Int. 1984, 30, 553.
110. Gruden, N. Nutr. Reports Int. 1983, 28, 473.
111. Sahagian, B.M.; Harding-Barlow, I.; Perry, H.M., Jr. J. Nutr. 1967, 93, 291.
112. Stacey, N.H.; Klaassen, C.D. J. Toxicol. Environ. Health 1981, 7, 149.
113. Suzuki, K.T.; Yaguchi, K.; Onuki, R.; Nishikawa, M.; Yamada, Y.K. J. Toxicol. Environ. Health 1983, 11, 713.
114. Jacobs, R.M.; Lee Jones, A.O.; Spivey Fox, M.R.; Lener, J. Proc. Soc. Exp. Biol. Med. 1983, 172 34.
115. Gruden, N. In Heavy Metals in the Environment, Lekkas, T.D., Ed.; Athens, 1985; Vol. 1, p. 676.

RECEIVED April 29, 1987

Chapter 8

Absorption Studies of Manganese from Milk Diets in Suckling Rats

Wai-Yee Chan[1-3], M. Hassan Raghib[1], and Owen M. Rennert[1-3]

[1]Department of Pediatrics, University of Oklahoma Health Sciences Center,
Oklahoma City, OK 73190
[2]Department of Biochemistry, University of Oklahoma Health Sciences Center,
Oklahoma City, OK 73190
[3]Department of Molecular Biology, University of Oklahoma Health Sciences Center,
Oklahoma City, OK 73190

Absorption of Manganese (Mn) from rat milk, human milk, bovine milk and infant formula by suckling rats was comparable even though the endogenous Mn content of these milk diets was different. Studies showed that absorption of Mn from all milk diets decreased with advancing age of the suckling rats. Using suckling rats it was shown that the decline in Mn absorption with age followed three stages with the changes occurring at 10 to 13 days and 20 days postnatal. A switching from duodenum to jejunum as being the site of maximal Mn absorption with advancing age of the suckling rat was also demonstrated by both in vivo and in vitro experiments. Enhanced absorption of Mn from bovine milk and infant formula rather than human milk was demonstrated by in vitro studies.

Manganese is an essential mineral required for normal growth and development (1,2). In the neonatal stage, the only dietary source of Mn for the infant is the mother's milk or its substitutes such as bovine milk or infant formulas. The relative bioavailability of most trace minerals in bovine milk and infant formulas as compared to human milk is not known. Very often even though deficiency might not have been reported in infants, an essential element is added to the breast milk substitute because it is known to be important for healthy growth of the infant. The Mn concentration of human milk is much lower than that found in bovine milk and infant formula (3). However, absolute quantity may not reflect the biologically effective level of Mn for absorption. For example, the high Mn requirement in poultry might be the result of inhibition of Mn absorption by high levels of calcium and phosphorus in the diet (4). In rats low levels of calcium and iron in the diet were associated with increased Mn absorption (4). Previous studies by Chan and associates using everted small intestinal sacs from adult rats demonstrated a difference in the bioavailability of Mn from human milk, bovine milk and infant formula (5). This was not totally surprising since the bioavailability of several other essential trace minerals has also been reported to be different in different types of milk. One well investigated case is that of iron. Using extrinsically tagged milk, the bioavailability of iron in human milk was found to be five to ten times greater

0097–6156/87/0354–0080$06.00/0

than that in infant formula even though the latter had a significantly higher iron content (6,7). Besides dietary components, the absorption of the mineral could also be affected by the age of the suckling infant. A number of examples were reported in the nutrition literature. A decrease in zinc (8), [95]Nb (9), [115]Cd (10), lead, cadmium and mercury (11) absorption was reported to occur in older rats when compared to younger animals.

Infant formulas are supplemented with Mn and other trace elements in the form of inorganic salts. Whether these supplemented minerals have different bioavailabilities from their counterparts found naturally in human milk or bovine milk has not been extensively investigated. Chan and associates previously reported that Mn was bound to different molecules in human milk, bovine milk and infant formula (12). Inadequate or excessive intake of Mn has severe effects especially during infancy (1,13). It is therefore important to evaluate the bioavailability of Mn in different milk diets. To achieve this aim, suckling rats and everted intestinal sacs derived from these animals were used as systems to study the absorption of Mn from rat milk, human milk, bovine milk and infant formula. Effect of age on Mn absorption in suckling rat pups from various milk diets was also investigated. Some of the data presented in this article have been reported previously (14-17).

Materials and Methods

Animals. Sprague-Dawley female rats raised on regular chow (Way Rodent Blox 8604) were bred at the Animal Facility of the University of Oklahoma Health Sciences Center. Females were mated with males of the same strain. Pups were kept with their dams from birth to the time of the experiment. Pups were separated from their dams and fasted for 14 hours before each experiment.

Milk. Human breast milk was obtained from volunteers and fresh raw bovine milk was obtained from local farms. Raw milk was used instead of pasteurized milk in order to preserve the Mn binding ligands in their natural form. The infant formula used was regular Similac (Ross Laboratories). Fresh rat milk was obtained from lactating female rats 8-12 days after parturition as described previously (17).

In Vivo Manganese Absorption Studies. Eight to thirteen day old suckling rats were used for these experiments. Milk samples (0.1 to 0.2 ml) were incubated with carrier free ^{54}MnCl$_2$ (New England Nuclear) buffered with 0.1 M sodium bicarbonate, pH 7.4 for 2 hours at room temperature. The final isotope concentration of ^{54}Mn was 5 μCi/ml milk. This method has been shown to label endogenous Mn binding ligands successfully (12). To eliminate individual variation to the maximum extent, only litters of a minimum of 8 pups were used for an experiment. At least 2 pups from the same litter were allocated to each diet category in any given feeding experiment and each experiment was repeated three or more times. Pups were fed by gastric intubation with 0.1 to 0.2 ml of extrinsically labeled milk as described previously (16). Amount of fed radioactivity was quantitated by whole body counting of the animal for 1 minute in a gamma counter after each feeding. If the pups were too large to allow whole body counting, the total amount of ^{54}Mn fed was calculated from the amount and specific activity of the milk sample fed. Absorption of ^{54}Mn was quantitated three hours after feeding by counting the digestive tract and the carcass with and without the liver.

In Vitro Manganese Absorption Studies. Rats of 10, 13 and 15 days of age were fasted 12 to 14 hours before sacrificing. The small intestine was removed and washed thoroughly with ice-cold physiological saline solution (0.9 % NaCl). Segments of 2 to 2.5 cm of the duodenum or jejunum were everted as described previously (18). After tying one end, the intestinal segment was filled with 50 to 100 µl of oxygenated modified Krebs-Ringer solution (135 mM NaCl, 5 mM glucose and 10 mM Tris, pH 7.4). The everted intestinal sacs were incubated for one hour at 37°C in 2.5 ml of either human milk, bovine milk or infant formula containing 0.5 µCi ^{54}Mn/ml.

Analytical Methods.   Manganese content of milk samples was measured in triplicate by flameless atomic absorption spectrophotometry using a Perkin-Elmer model 703 Atomic Absorption Spectrophotometer equipped with a HGA 500 graphite furnace and an AS-1 autosampler. Standards were run after every third sample.   Manganese-54 radioactivity of milk and tissue samples were quantitated by using a Beckman 8000 deep-well gamma counter. Due to the geometrical difference of a whole carcass and the liver in the deep-well, the carcass counts of the small and large suckling rats were multiplied by correction factors determined experimentally. Protein content of milk samples was determined by the method of Lowry et al. (19).

Statistical Analysis.   Testing for significant differences between groups was done by analysis of variance according to the SAS User's Guide 1977 edition, SAS Institute, Raleigh, N.C. The results of several experiments were combined and the differences among the means of the various categories were subjected to analysis of variance allowing for an unequal number of animals in each group as described (17). All dependent variables were consistent with respect to the presence or absence of the missing values. The probability of occurrence by chance of $p < 0.05$ was accepted as significant.

Results and Discussion

In Vivo Manganese Absorption.   Recovery of ^{54}Mn in all experiments was above 98% (results not shown).   No loss of the isotope was encountered during the experimental period.   Previous experiments established the optimum fasting time prior to feeding to be 12 to 14 hours and the optimum assimilation time to be 3 hours (16).   With a similar protocol the whole body retention of ^{54}Mn in 9 day old rat pups was found to be similar regardless of whether human milk, bovine milk, infant formula or rat milk was fed. The results are presented in Table I.   No statistically significant ($p < 0.05$) difference existed among the four milk diets.   Similar observation was also reported recently by another laboratory (20). In all cases examined, liver retained over 65 % of the absorbed ^{54}Mn indicating that liver Mn might be as good an index for assessing Mn absorption as Mn content of the gut-free carcass.   This observation is not surprising since both Cotzias et al. (21) and Papavasiliou et al. (22) have shown that the liver is responsible for regulation of Mn homeostasis and Black et al. (23) in a recent report have shown a linear increase in liver Mn in a bioavailability study of Mn in the chicken.

Human milk contained relatively less Mn when compared to the other milk diets examined. The endogenous Mn concentrations of human milk, bovine milk, infant formula and rat milk used in the present studies as determined by flameless atomic absorption spectrophotometry were 8 ± 3, 30 ± 5, 73 ± 4, 148 ± 18 µg/liter respectively.   It is possible that the higher concentrations of endogenous Mn in infant formula and rat milk might compete with the added ^{54}Mn for transport during the experiments.   However, the addition of nonradioactive Mn in the form of $MnCl_2$ to both human and bovine milk to concentrations up to 150 µg/litre had little or no effect on the absorption of ^{54}Mn by 10 day old rats from these two kinds of milk (results not shown). These results suggested that at the level of carrier free ^{54}Mn used in the experiments described in this report absorption of Mn would be proportional to the absorption of ^{54}Mn.

Table I. Retention of ^{54}Mn from Various Milk Diets by 9 Day Old Suckling Rats[a]

Milk Diet	N[b]	Mean ^{54}Mn as % of Dose		
		Carcass with Liver[c]	Liver	Per Gm Liver
Human Milk	13	31 ± 7[d]	19 ± 6	46 ± 12
Bovine Milk	12	28 ± 6	19 ± 7	42 ± 12
Infant Formula	13	31 ± 7	19 ± 4	43 ± 12
Rat Milk	15	29 ± 6	19 ± 5	42 ± 10

a.   Results of 5 different feeding experiments were combined for each of the milk diets examined.
b.   Number of pups.
c.   Whole body minus stomach and digestive tract.
d.   Means ± standard deviations.

Effect of Age of Suckling Rats on Absorption of Milk Manganese In Vivo.
Retention of absorbed milk Mn in the carcass was affected by the age of the suckling neonate. Results are presented in Figure 1. Each bar in the histogram represents results obtained from at least 10 pups. Manganese-54 radioactivity was expressed as % of dose. Both means and standard deviations of the means are shown. There appeared to be three stages in the course of the decline of Mn absorption with increasing age of the suckling rat. This change was observed for all three milk diets (human milk, bovine milk and infant formula) and appeared to be independent of the nature of the milk diet. The amount of ^{54}Mn retained by the carcass of the 10 day old and younger rats was comparable with no significant difference ($p < 0.05$) regardless of the type of milk diet fed. The decline in ^{54}Mn absorption with age before 10 day postnatal was very small if existed. The first and milder drop occurred between 10 to 13 day postnatal. The difference between the amount of ^{54}Mn in the carcass of 10 and 13 day old rats was significant ($p < 0.05$). The decrease in ^{54}Mn absorption into the carcass of 13 and 20 day old rats was gradual but steeper than the change occurring in the first stage. There was a drastic decline in the retention of ^{54}Mn in the carcass of rats older than 20 days postnatal. For rats older than 20 days postnatal, Figure 1 only shows the data for 30 day old rats. Absorption of ^{54}Mn in 23 and 25 day old rats was similar to that in 30 day old rats. It is interesting to notice that rats usually wean at around 20 days postnatal.

The difference in carcass ^{54}Mn radioactivity between 10 and 20 day old rats was approximately three fold. This difference in ^{54}Mn absorption between the two age groups was also reflected in the amount of ^{54}Mn retained by the intestinal tissues of these two groups. In this experiment eleven 10 day old rats were fed infant formula labeled with ^{54}Mn. The rats were sacrificed three hours after feeding. The intestine was removed and the lumen content flushed out by washing the tissue several times with ice-cold physiological saline until a

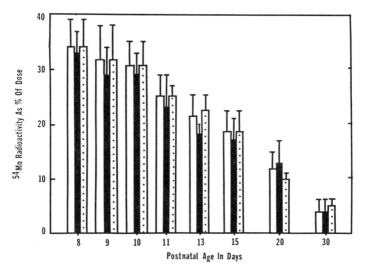

Figure 1.   Effect of Age on the Incorporation of ^{54}Mn into the Carcass
of Suckling Rats Fed Various Milk Diets

☐ Human Milk; ■ Bovine Milk; ⌜•••••⌝ Infant Formula

constant reading was obtained when the tissue was counted after two consecutive washes. The same experiment was repeated with six 20 day old rats. The means and standard deviations of the means of ^{54}Mn radioactivity (as % of dose) retained by the duodenum, jejunum, ileum and the large intestine for the 10 day old rats were 17.1 $\pm$ 3.5, 1.7 $\pm$ 0.6, 0.5 $\pm$ 0.2, and 0.4 $\pm$ 0.2 respectively. Significantly less (p $<$ 0.05) ^{54}Mn was found in the duodenum of 20 day old rats (1.2 $\pm$ 1.0) while the other segments of the intestine of rats of this age group retained more ^{54}Mn when compared with the 10 day old rats (2.4 $\pm$ 1.4 for jejunum, 2.2 $\pm$ 1.2 for ileum, and 1.4 $\pm$ 0.8 for large intestine). The difference in duodenal tissue ^{54}Mn radioactivity between rats of the two age groups was even bigger when they were expressed as % of dose per gram of wet tissue (11.8 $\pm$ 6.1 for 10 day old rats and 0.51 $\pm$ 0.24 for 20 day old rats, both values were for the whole duodenum plus 1/3 of jejunum). In both the 10 and 20 day old rats more than 55 % of the duodenal tissue ^{54}Mn radioactivity was retained by the brush border cells (57.5 % for 10 day old rats and 55.4 % for 20 day old rats).

Not only the site of maximal absorption of Mn but also the emptying time of milk in the stomach and various sections of the intestine varies with age of the suckling rat. Ten and 20 day old rats were fed 0.2 ml of human milk, bovine milk or infant formula labeled with ^{54}Mn. Three hours after feeding, the rats were sacrificed. The gastrointestinal tract was removed and the stomach, small intestine and large intestine were counted separately before and after the lumen contents were emptied. Regardless of the type of milk diet, passage of milk from the stomach to the small intestine and from the small to the large intestine was faster in 20 days old rats than in 10 day old rats. The relative distribution of ^{54}Mn among the stomach, small intestine and large intestine was very similar for all three milk diets examined. For 10 day old rats at three hours after feeding with infant formula the percent distribution of total gastrointestinal tract ^{54}Mn radioactivity among the stomach, small intestine and large intestine was 32.4 $\pm$ 4.2, 62.5 $\pm$ 4.4, and 5.1 $\pm$ 3.6 respectively (values represent means $\pm$ standard deviations for 8 rats). On the other hand in 20 day old rats, the stomach only retained 11.9 $\pm$ 2.4 % while the small intestine and large intestine retained 75.8 $\pm$ 6.1 % and 12.3 $\pm$ 6.6 % of the total ^{54}Mn radioactivity in the gastrointestinal tract, respectively (Values represent means $\pm$ standard deviations for 8 rats). Even though in 10 day old rats the percent distribution of ^{54}Mn in flushed tissue of the different sections of the gastrointestinal tract at 3 hours after feeding did not vary with the nature of the milk diets, detailed analysis of the tissue distribution of ^{54}Mn among various sections of the small intestine showed that duodenum always retained the majority of tissue ^{54}Mn (11.5 $\pm$ 5.8 % for human milk, 8.2 $\pm$ 4.9 % for bovine milk and 13.5 $\pm$ 3.5 % for infant formula, all value as % of dose). However, if jejunal tissue ^{54}Mn contents were compared, the jejunum of rats fed bovine milk retained more ^{54}Mn (4.0 $\pm$ 1.2 % out of 13.4 $\pm$ 2.3 % of total administered dose of ^{54}Mn retained by intestinal tissue including duodenum, jejunum and ileum) than rats fed either human milk (2.0 $\pm$ 1.3 % out of 15.3 $\pm$ 2.8 % for total intestinal tissue) or infant formula (2.1 $\pm$ 1.2 % out of 16.3 $\pm$ 5.5 % for total intestinal tissue).

The pronounced effect of age on the ability of the suckling rats to retain dietary Mn observed in the present study has also been reported by others (20,24-26). This developmental change in the absorption of Mn from milk could be related to the change in the absorption mechanism in response to lactational change in the constituents of milk or because of intestinal maturation. Naturally, change in intestinal resecretion of absorbed Mn could also be a factor (Weigand, E.; Kirchgessner, M. Proc. 5th Int. Symp. Trace Element

Metab. Man and Animal, in press). Occurrence of developmental stage specific binding ligand in the intestine for a particular nutrient has also been suggested (27). Even though convincing examples are lacking, the present studies cannot rule this out as a factor causing the observed change in Mn absorption with age in suckling rats. A change in the absorption mechanism of Mn with age is obviated by the observation that a larger amount of ^{54}Mn was retained by the jejunum and ileum in comparison to the duodenum in older (20 day old) suckling rats than in younger ones. In adult rats the major Mn absorption site has also been reported to be the jejunum by other researchers (28). This switching of maximal Mn absorption site from duodenum to jejunum with age could be one of the reasons for the decline of Mn absorption in older rats. The contribution from the intestinal excretion of Mn due to bile also should not be neglected (29). On the other hand, the observed change in the passage of milk through the gastrointestinal tract might be the consequence of an age related change in the stomach function of suckling rats.

**Table II. Relative Importance of Duodenum and Jejunum
In In Vitro Manganese Absorption**

Age in Days	N[a]	Milk Diet	Ratio of Mean Serosal Fluid ^{54}Mn % In Duodenal Sac/Jejunal Sac
10	4	Human Milk	1.37[b]
	4	Bovine Milk	1.24
	4	Infant Formula	1.38
13	4	Human Milk	1.56
	4	Bovine Milk	1.81
	4	Infant Formula	0.97
15	4	Human Milk	1.86
	4	Bovine Milk	0.65
	4	Infant Formula	0.92

a. Number of animals in each group.
b. Values presented were ratio of the mean value of ^{54}Mn radioactivity recovered in the serosal fluid expressed as percent of dose per gm wet tissue of the duodenal sac to that of the jejunal sac.

In Vitro Manganese Absorption. To further examine the relative importance of duodenal and jejunal Mn absorption at different ages in rats, in vitro experiments were performed with different segments of the intestine. To account for the difference in tissue mass of the intestine at different ages, the ratio of the percent of dose of ^{54}Mn per gm wet tissue recovered in the serosal fluid of the everted duodenal and jejunal sac was computed. The results are presented in Table II. Duodenum played a more important role in ^{54}Mn absorption in younger rats (10 day old). This is true for all three milk diets examined. Except in the case of human milk, there appeared to be a switching of maximal Mn absorption site from the duodenum to jejunum with increasing age of the suckling rat. This observation coincided with the observation made in in vivo studies of Mn absorption with infant formula. The duodenum appeared to remain the major absorptive site for Mn even in rats of 15 days of age.

Table III. In Vitro Absorption Studies of Manganese
from Different Milk Diets

Age in Days	N[a]	Milk Diet	^{54}Mn as % of Dose/Gm Intestinal Sac	
			Serosal Fluid[b]	Intestinal Tissue[b]
	4	Human Milk	23.7 ± 10.0[c]	295.6 ± 75.7
10	4	Bovine Milk	56.6 ± 21.6	332.3 ± 44.2
	4	Infant Formula	52.8 ± 18.3	516.7 ± 186.3
	4	Human Milk	8.0 ± 2.4	119.2 ± 18.1
13	4	Bovine Milk	11.4 ± 2.0	100.4 ± 20.0
	4	Infant Formula	11.4 ± 2.3	121.1 ± 24.6
	4	Human Milk	6.2 ± 2.0	63.6 ± 16.3
15	4	Bovine Milk	13.4 ± 1.3	157.0 ± 11.9
	4	Infant Formula	6.2 ± 0.8	98.7 ± 14.0

a. Number of animals in each group.
b. Obtained by combining the duodenal and jejunal sac results.
c. Means ± standard deviations.

The effect of age of the animal on the transport of milk Mn across the intestinal wall was also investigated with this in vitro system. Radioactivity of ^{54}Mn recovered in the intestinal tissue and serosal fluid when different milk diets were incubated with everted sacs derived from suckling rats of different ages was expressed as percent of dose per gm of wet tissue in these two compartments. The results are presented in Table III.

For all three milk diets tested the absorption of Mn, in terms of both being transported to the serosal fluid and being taken up by the intestinal tissue, was higher in younger rats. This agreed with the results obtained in in vivo studies with the suckling rats. Further analysis of the data showed that the uptake of ^{54}Mn into intestinal tissue was higher from bovine milk and infant formula than from human milk. This is true when the intestinal tissues were derived from rats of 10 or 15 days of age. The transport of ^{54}Mn to serosal fluid across the intestinal sac was also significantly higher (p < 0.05) from bovine milk and infant formula than from human milk regardless of the age of the rats from which the intestinal tissues were derived with the exception of formula with 15 day old rats. This significant difference in the transport and uptake of Mn from bovine milk and human milk is consistent with the observation previously reported using everted intestinal sacs from adult rats (5) but is different from results of the in vivo absorption studies presented above and a recent report from another laboratory (26). The cause of this discrepancy between the results of the in vivo and in vitro experiments is not clear. One possibility is that gastrointestinal processing of the milk diet plays an important role in the absorption of Mn. This is implicated by the results of the study of the passage of milk through the gastrointestinal tract. The role of intestinal secretion of Mn also cannot be neglected. Naturally, there is also the possibility that the mechanism of Mn absorption in the in vivo situation might be altered in the in vitro system. This therefore poses an important question concerning the validity of everted intestinal sacs for studying the absorption of nutrients.

Conclusion

The present study showed that the absorption of Mn from milk in suckling rats is largely regulated by the age, or in other words, the developmental stage of the animal. Even though rat milk, bovine milk and infant formula contained higher amounts of Mn than human breast milk, absorption of Mn from these four types of milk is comparable in suckling rats. These results suggest that supplementation of infant formulas with excessive Mn would not guarantee an increased supply of the mineral to the infant. This contention is supported by reports that serum manganese levels were not higher in formula-fed infants than in breast-fed infants (30,31).

A decline in absorption of Mn with advancing age of the suckling rats has been shown. This change in Mn absorption appeared to be correlated with the switching of the site of maximal absorption. In younger animals the duodenum is more active in Mn absorption while in older animals the jejunum plays a more important role. This switching of absorption site is also demonstrable using everted intestinal sacs from rats of different ages.

The nature of the milk diet does not appear to have any effect on the absorption of Mn by suckling rats in the present study. However, in vitro studies did show a difference in uptake of Mn from different milk diets. This suggests that other physiological factors regulating intestinal Mn absorption overshadow the difference in the transport of Mn from the different milk diets across the mucosal/serosal membranes.

Acknowledgments

We would like to thank the mothers of the La Leche League of Oklahoma City for providing us with some of the milk samples used in these studies. We would also like to thank Ms. Greta Shepherd for typing the manuscript. This study was supported by NIH grants HD 16730 and HD 21793 awarded to W.Y.C.

Literature Cited

1. Shaw, J.C.L. Am. J. Dis. Child. 1980, 13, 74-87.
2. Hurley, L.S. In Clinical, Biochemical and Nutritional Aspects of Trace Elements; Prasad, A.S., Ed.; Alan R. Liss, Inc.: New York, 1982; p. 369.
3. Committee on Nutrition Pediatric Nutrition Handbook; American Academy of Pediatrician: Evanston, 1979; p. 92.
4. Forbes, R.M.; Erdman, J.W., Jr. Ann. Rev. Nutr. 1983, 3, 213-231.
5. Chan, W.Y.; Bates, J.M., Jr.; Rennert, O.M.: Mahmood, A.S.; Torres-Pinedo, R. Life Sci. 1984, 35, 2415-2419.
6. Saarinen, U.M.; Siimes, M.A.; Dallman, P.R. J. Pediat. 1977, 41, 36-39.
7. McMillan, J.A.; Oski, F.A.; Lourie, G.; Tomarelli, R.M.; Landaw, S.A. Pediatrics 1977, 60, 896-900.
8. Shah, B.G. In Progress in Clinical and Biological Research; Alan R. Liss, Inc.: New York, 1981; Vol. 77, p. 199.
9. Mraz, F.R.; Eisele, G.R. Pediat. Res. 1977, 69, 591-593.
10. Sasser, L.B.; Jarboe, G.E. Toxicol. Appl. Pharmacol. 1977, 41, 423-431.
11. Kostial, K.; Robar, L; Blanusa, M.; Landeka, M. Proc. Nutr. Soc. 1977, 38, 251-256.
12. Chan, W.Y.; Bates, J.M., Jr.; Rennert, O.M. J. Nutr 1982, 112, 642-651.
13. Collipp, P.J.: Chen, S.Y.; Martinsky, S. Ann. Nutr. Metab. 1983, 27, 488-494.

14. Raghib, M.H.; Chan, W.Y.; Rennert, O.M. Fed. Proc. 1984, 43, 489.
15. Raghib, M.H.; Chan, W.Y.; Rennert, O.M. Fed. Proc. 1985, 44, 1850.
16. Raghib, M.H.; Chan, W.Y.; Rennert, O.M. Nutr. Rep. Int. 1985, 32, 1201-1210.
17. Raghib, M.H.; Chan, W.Y.; Rennert, O.M. Brit. J. Nutr. 1986, 55, 49-58.
18. Wilson, T.H.; Wiseman, G. J. Physiol. 1954, 123, 116-125.
19. Lowry, O.H.; Rosenbrough, N.J.; Farr, A.L.; Randall, R.J. J. Biol. Chem. 1951, 193, 265-275.
20. Keen, C.L.; Bell, J.G.; Lonnerdal, B. J. Nutr. 1986, 116, 395-402.
21. Cotzias, G.C.; Papavasiliou, P.S. Nature (London) 1964, 201, 828-829.
22. Papavasiliou, P.S.; Miller, S.T.; Cotzias, G.C. Am. J. Physiol. 1966, 211, 211-216.
23. Black, J.R.; Ammerman, C.B.; Henry, P.R.; Miles, R.D. Nutr. Rep. Int. 1984, 29, 807-814.
24. Rehnberg, G.L.; Hein, J.F.; Carter, S.D.; Laskey, J.W. J. Toxicol. Environ. Health, 1980, 6, 217-226.
25. Rehnberg, G.L.; Hein, J.F.; Carter, S.D.; Laskey, J.W. J. Toxicol. Environ. Health, 1981, 7, 263-272.
26. Gruden, N. Nutr. Rep. Int. 1984, 30, 553-557.
27. Duncan, J.R.; Hurley, L.S. Am. J. Physiol. 1978, 235, E556-559.
28. Garcia-Aranda, J.A; Wapnir, R.A.; Lifshitz, F. J. Nutr. 1983, 113, 2601-2607.
29. Miller, S.T.; Cotzias, G.C.; Evert, H.A. Am. J. Physiol. 1975, 229, 1080-1084.
30. Stastny, D.; Vogel, R.S.; Picciano, M.F. Am. J. Clin. Nutr. 1984, 39, 872-878.
31. Craig, W.J. Nutr. Rep. Int. 1984, 30, 1003-1008.

RECEIVED January 28, 1987

Chapter 9

Manganese Requirements of Humans

Jeanne H. Freeland-Graves, Connie W. Bales[1], and Fares Behmardi

Division of Nutrition, University of Texas at Austin, Austin, TX 78712

The estimated safe and adequate daily dietary allowance for manganese (Mn) in adults and adolescents may be too low. In the past, dietary intakes were higher because whole grains were an essential component of the diet. But the larger proportion of meats and refined foods in current diets may lead to low dietary intakes of Mn. Since numerous studies have reported negative balances of the mineral in adults and adolescents consuming conventional foods, a higher dietary level is indicated. A new suggested range of 3.5-7 mg/day is based on a review of past and present studies.

The human requirement for manganese (Mn) is inferred from its essentiality in animals since gross deficiencies of the mineral have not been observed in free-living populations. However, there are reports of experimentally-induced deficiencies in humans and a number of cases of sub-optimal status.

Human Deficiencies

The first report of an experimentally-induced deficiency was by Doisy (1) who fed two subjects a formula diet that was deficient in vitamin K. One of the subjects developed a slight reddening of the hair, a scaly, transient dermatitis, depressed vitamin K-dependent clotting factors, and hypocholesterolemia. The symptoms were unresponsive to vitamin K but disappeared when a normal diet was resumed. When Doisey recalculated his purified diet, he realized that he had inadvertently omitted the manganese. The diet had contained a manganese level of only 0.34 mg/day and apparently had produced a manganese deficiency.

The second report was part of a metabolic balance study conducted in our laboratory (2). Seven males were fed a semi-purified diet containing 0.11 mg Mn/day for 39 days. On the 35th day, five of the seven subjects developed a finely scaling, minimally erythematous rash that primarily covered the upper torso, but also affected the groin area and lower extremities of some of the subjects. The rash was diagnosed as *Miliaria crystallina*, a condition in which sweat cannot be excreted through the surface of the skin and results in small, clear blisters filled with fluid. This rash was exacerbated during exercise when sweating occurred. After 2 days, the blisters broke

[1]Current address: Center for the Study of Aging and Human Development, Box 3003, Duke University, Durham, NC 27710

and the affected areas of the skin became dry and flaky. The skin cleared rapidly but manganese supplementation began on the fifth day following the outbreak of the rash.

A possible explanation for the transient dermatitis observed in both studies could be related to the requirement of manganese for the activity of glycosyltransferases and/or prolidase, enzymes that are necessary to maintain the integrity of the dermis. Glycosyltransfereases participate in the synthesis of glycosaminoglycans, compounds which form the mucopolysaccharides of collagen in the skin (3). Prolidase is an enzyme that catalyzes the breakdown of collagen in dermal fibroblasts. A genetic deficiency of prolidase leads to a severe dermititis with chronic cutaneous ulcers (4).

The subjects in our study also developed hypocholesterolemia. The decline in total plasma cholesterol during manganese depletion in both studies is presumably related to the need for manganese at several sites in the synthesis of cholesterol (5).

This same study observed elevated levels of serum calcium, phosphorus, and alkaline phosphatase activity in the subjects. These changes suggest that manganese was being mobilized from stores in bone. In rats fed a manganese deficient diet for 12 months, increased concentrations of serum calcium and phosphorus have also been observed. In addition, the bones of the rats had decreased concentrations of manganese and developed an osteoporotic condition (6). Whether or not a continued deficiency of manganese in humans would eventually lead to osteoporosis warrants further investigation.

Sub-optimal Status

A number of cases of suboptimal status of manganese have been observed. Hurry and Gibson (7) found children with phenylketonuria (PKU), galactosemia, and methylmalonic acidemia had lower concentrations of hair manganese than their age-matched controls, even though dietary intakes were comparable. Another study of children with PKU and maple syrup urine diseases reported significantly lower retentions of manganese compared to normal children (8). Lower retention and absorption of manganese have also been found in patients with exocrine pancreatic insufficiency (9). In epileptics, Tanaka (10) first reported significant decreases in whole blood manganese in approximately one-third of children having convulsive seizures compared to neurologically normal children. Low levels of blood manganese have also been found in two studies of adult epileptics (11,12). Papavasiliou et al. (11) reported that the low blood manganese was independent of the type of anticonvulsive drugs taken and related to the frequency of seizures. Carl et al. (12) did not confirm these correlations but did find higher whole blood manganese levels in patients whose epilepsy was a result of trauma compared to those with no history of trauma.

In contrast, *elevated* concentrations of whole blood manganese have been reported in patients with active rheumatoid arthritis or hydralazine syndrome (13), diseases that involve defects in collagen metabolism. The increased blood concentrations of manganese observed in these patients were surprising since they had slower body turnover rates of ^{54}Mn compared to controls. These investigators suggested that these patients had a relative deficiency of manganese due to an altered body distribution of the mineral. It should be noted that manganese supplementation has been used with success in treating humans and animals with hydralazine disease (14,15).

Balance Studies in Children and Adolescents

The first manganese balance study in humans was conducted in 1934 by Everson and Daniels (16) who studied children ages 3 to 5 years (Table 1). The children were fed

Table 1. Summary of manganese balance studies

| Subject | | Design | | Manganese | | | | |
Age yr	Sex	Days	Diet	Intake mg/d	Urinary mg/d	Fecal mg/d	Balance mg/d	Reference
3-5	M, F	7	Mixed	1.84- 5.03	0.007- 0.012	1.67- 4.04	+0.17- +0.97	(16)
6-10	F	30- 56	Varied protein	2.10- 4.84	- -	1.95- 3.55	+0.15- +1.29	(17)
7-9	M	30	Varied calcium & protein	2.13- 2.43	0.01- 0.02	1.97- 2.23	+0.15- +0.18	(18)
7-9	F	8 12	Varied calcium & nitrogen	1.91- 2.06	0.010- 0.011	1.87- 2.05	+0.01- +0.26	(19)
0.02		3	Breastfed	0.007	0.000	0.04	+0.03	(20)
0.25- 8.5	M, F	11	Mixed	1.15[a]	0.02	0.97	+0.16	(8)
12-14	F	30	Varied protein & zinc	3.00	-	3.52	-0.5	(21)
19-30	M	6-9	Whole wheat	4.2- 22.5	- -	4.1- 10.9	+0.1- +11.6	(22)
24-28	M	6	Fish	10.70	-	7.33	+3.37	(23)
24-28	M	6-9	Rice & fish Whole wheat Sago	9.81 9.61 0.71	- - -	6.60 6.33 1.76	+3.21 +3.28 -1.05	(24)
Adult	F	-	White flour Whole wheat	2.45 8.67	0.08 0.06	2.35 8.36	+0.02 +0.26	(25)
18-21	F	41	Varied protein	3.70	0.20	1.97	+1.54	(26)
20-29	M	35	Vegetarian	7.07	0.21	3.53	+3.34	(27)
23-25	M	347 347	Self-chosen	3.3 5.5	0.04 0.05	2.5 3.0	+0.80 +2.50	(28)
19-22		27	Mixed	2.78	0.01	2.45	+0.32[b]	(29)

Table 1. Continued

Subject		Design		Intake	Excretion		Balance	Reference
					Manganese			
Age yr	Sex	Days	Diet	mg/d	Urinary mg/d	Fecal mg/d	mg/d	
Adult	M	21	Varied calcium & flouride	2.13-2.23	0.02-0.02	2.27-2.50	-0.15-[b] -0.28	(30)
19.2-25.6	M	12	Varied protein & phosphorus	3.00-3.14	- -	2.66-3.14	-0.10-[b] +0.45	(31)
Adult	M	20	Varied tin	3.28	-	-	-0.13[b]	(32)
20-24	M	11	Indian foods	5.4-17.5	0.03-0.03	5.3-14.4	+0.1-[b] +3.1	(33)
Adult	M	11	Indian foods	3.60-8.37	0.01-0.04	3.49-6.54	-0.30-[b] +2.24	(34)
22-32	M	21 28	Mixed	13.9 15.0	- -	14.2 14.1	-0.7[b] +1.1	(35)
Adult	M	45	Dephytinized bran	4.1	-	4.8	-0.7[b]	(36)
Adult	M,F	28	Mixed	3.00	-	-	-0.16[b]	(37)
Adult	M,F	7	Vegetarian Self-selected	3.6-5.1	- -	- -	-0.5-[b] -1.1	(38)
Adult	M	7	Self-selected	4.28	-	4.98	-0.70[b]	(39)
Adult	F	7	Varied iron	3.89	- -	3.45-4.02	-0.13-[b] +0.44	(40)
19-22	M	39 5 5	Semi-purified	0.11 1.53 2.55	0.002[c] 0.004[c] 0.004[c]	0.12[c] 0.66[c] 1.51[c]	-0.02[b,d] +0.84[b,e] +1.02[b,e]	(2)
19-20	M	38 21 14 21 11	Mixed	1.21 2.06 2.65 2.89 3.79	0.001[c] 0.001[c] 0.001[c] 0.004[c] 0.002[c]	1.24[c] 2.03[c] 2.47[c] 2.86[c] 3.02[c]	-0.09[b,f,g] -0.02[b,f] +0.14[b,d] -0.08[b,d] +0.85[b,f]	

[a]Calculated for a 20 kg child. [b]Analyzed by flame atomic absorption spectroscopy. [c]Analyzed by graphite furnace atomic absorption spectroscopy. [d]Includes 0.02 mg integumental loss/day. [e]Includes 0.03 mg integumental loss/ day. [f]Includes 0.01 mg integumental loss/ day. [g]Submitted for publication.

three levels of manganese, 1.84, 2.52, and 5.03 mg/day, for a one week period. On these dietary levels, balances were determined to be 0.17, 0.50, and 0.97 mg Mn, respectively.

Over 30 years passed before subsequent studies were conducted in children. In 1967, Engel et al. (17) collected data from girls, ages 6 to 10, fed diets that varied in protein quantity and type. Positive manganese balances from 0.15 to 1.29 mg/day were observed in diets that ranged from 2.10 to 4.84 Mn mg/day. The influence of protein on balance could not be ascertained since the dietary manganese was substantially increased by the substitution of plant protein for animal protein sources. In their next study of pre-adolescent girls (18), the diets varied in calcium from 260 to 620 mg/day and in protein from 25 to 46 g/day. No significant effects of these dietary manipulations on balance were observed. Consumption of diets that contained from 2.13 to 2.43 mg Mn/day produced positive balances of 0.15 to 0.18 mg Mn/day. In their final study (19), the diets varied in calcium from 300 to 1300 mg/day and dietary nitrogen was elevated from supplements of ammonium citrate or synthetic limiting amino acids. Manganese balance was not affected except from the addition of ammonium citrate in the absence of a calcium supplement. A slight improvement in balance was seen but it was negated by the addition of a 1000 mg calcium supplement. Dietary intakes of 1.91 and 2.06 mg Mn/day produced positive balances that ranged from 0.005 to 0.258 Mn/day.

The manganese balance of ten 6-day old breast-fed infants was measured for a 3-day period by Widdowson in 1969 (20). For a 3.5 kg infant, an intake of 7 μg/day produced a negative balance of 31 μg. Alexander et al. (8) studied the manganese requirements of children, 3 months to 9 years, fed normal and synthetic diets. From calculation of their data, a manganese intake of 1.15 mg/day in a 20 kg child would produce a positive retention of 0.16 mg.

The only manganese balance study in adolescents was conducted by Greger et al. (21) who fed diets containing 3.0 mg Mn/day for 30 days. The diets varied in the levels of zinc (7.4 and 13.4 mg) and defatted soy protein and meat. These diets produced negative balances in 13 out of 14 girls. The mean balance was -0.5 mg Mn/day and was not affected by zinc levels or substitution of soy protein for meat.

Balance Studies in Adults

Basu and Malakar (22) were the first investigators to study manganese balance in adults. Positive manganese balances, ranging from 0.1 to 11.6 mg/day, were found when fecal excretion of three men was measured. However the dietary levels of manganese were high, ranging from 4.2 to 22.5 mg/day, because of the inclusion of whole wheat in some of the diets.

High intakes of manganese were also reported in two studies of Indian diets. In the first study (23), a mean balance of 3.37 mg Mn/day was reported for subjects consuming typical diets with a mean level of 10.7 mg Mn/day. In the second study (24), dietary levels ranged from 6.42 to 13.81 mg Mn/day. Mean manganese balances of 3.21 and 3.28 mg/day were found for rice-fish and whole wheat-based diets that had contained 9.81 and 9.61 mg Mn, respectively. The type of fat that was used in the preparation of the diets had no effect on manganese balance. Both manganese intake (0.71 mg/day) and balance (-1.05 mg/day) decreased substantially when a sago diet was fed. De (23) observed that manganese balance became more and more positive as dietary levels of the mineral increased.

In 1941, Kent and McCance (25) measured balance in three subjects eating mixed diets containing 1.72, 2.21, and 6.64 mg Mn/day. In the first 7-day period measured, mean respective balances of -0.05, +0.16, and -0.39 mg Mn were found. In two other subjects, substitution of white for brown flour decreased the manganese intake from 8.67 to 2.45 mg/day and the daily balance from 0.26 to 0.02 mg.

The first study of college women was conducted by North et al. (26) who fed conventional foods that varied in protein content from 37 to 76 g/day. The daily intake of manganese averaged 3.7 mg/day and produced a mean positive balance of 1.54 mg Mn. Changing the daily protein level had no effect. In 1965, Lang et al. (27) fed college men a diet containing an even higher intake of manganese, 7.07 mg/day. This produced a higher positive balance, 3.34 mg. Substitution of vegetable protein for skim milk powder did not influence manganese retention. The researchers observed that variations in height and weight were responsible for some of the variation in retention; however, when these variables were held constant, retention rates still varied considerably between subjects.

The longest balance study measuring manganese was conducted by Tipton et al. (28) who collected duplicate diets and all urinary and fecal excreta of two men for 347 days. The self-chosen diets of the two men contained an average of 3.3 and 5.5 mg Mn/day and produced positive balances of 0.8 and 2.5 mg/day, respectively.

McLeod and Robinson (29) published the first manganese balance study in adults in which atomic absorption spectrophotometry was the method of analysis. A positive balance of 0.32 mg/day was found for young women consuming a mixed diet containing 2.78 mg Mn. However, the diet consisted solely of meat and ice cream with tea and coffee, and in two subjects, orange juice.

A more nutritionally-adequate diet was fed by Spencer et al. (30) who fed eight adult males diets that contained from 2.13 to 2.23 mg Mn/day. Respective negative balances of -0.15 to -0.28 mg Mn/day were reported. Varying the level of calcium from 200 to 1500 mg/day or administering 10 mg flouride had no influence on the balance of manganese.

In 1980, Greger and Snedeker (31) fed eight adult males diets that contained varying levels of protein (8.1 and 24.1 g nitrogen) and phosphorus (1,010 and 2,525 mg) for four 12-day periods. Both small negative and positive balances of -0.10 to +0.45 mg resulted when diets contained between 3.00 to 3.14 mg Mn/day. Varying the level of protein or phosphorus had no effect. The same laboratory found similar results in a study (32) investigating the influence of low (0.1 mg) and high (50 mg) levels of tin on mineral balance. A small mean negative balance of -0.13 mg Mn occurred from a mixed diet containing 3.28 mg Mn/day. The level of tin did not affect manganese balance.

Rao and Rao determined manganese balances in two studies of typical Indian diets. In the first study (33), diets representative of different geographical locations in India were fed to six subjects for five 11-day periods. The diets contained from 5.4 to 17.5 mg Mn/day and produced positive balances of 0.1 to 3.1 mg Mn/day. A legume-based vegetarian diet produced lower absorption rates of manganese compared to those that included fish or meat. In the second study (34), a basal vegetarian diet supplemented with regional foods was fed to five men for five 11-day periods. Dietary intakes of 3.6 to 4.0 mg Mn/day produced negative balances of -0.30 to 0.39 mg Mn. Increasing the dietary level from 4.31 to 8.37 mg/day led to postive balances of 0.08 to 2.24 mg Mn. The reported rate of absorption for manganese was 43%.

The absorption rate reported by Rao and Rao (34) is relatively high considering the elevated concentrations of fiber and phytate that are usually present in vegetarian diets. Schwartz et al. (35) determined manganese absorption rates of -2.0 to 7.6 % for high fiber, high phytate diets. In this study, the fiber and phytate levels of the diet were increased by the daily inclusion of four slices of whole wheat bread and three bran muffins. Despite high dietary intakes of 13.9 and 15.0 mg Mn/day, balances of -0.7 and 1.1 mg Mn were found. In another study in which 8.6 g dephytinized wheat bran was added to the diet of six men for 45 days, a mean negative balance of -0.7 mg Mn/day was found on an intake of 4.1 mg/day (36).

Patterson et al. (37) measured the manganese balance of 28 free-living adults who provided duplicates of their self-selected diet for one week periods during the four seasons of the year. The subjects were in negative balance ($\bar{x}$ = -0.16 mg) on a daily intake of 3.00 mg/day during each season. However, the data were complicated by an approximate 15% reduction in caloric intake during the collection week. Apparently, the subjects decreased their normal quantity of food. This abrupt lowering of caloric intake during collection periods was suggested as a probable cause of the negative balances observed.

Two other studies measured manganese balances in duplicate 7-day composite diets. The first study found that diets of 59 adult free-living vegetarians contained 3.6, 4.8, 4.3, and 5.1 mg Mn/day in female and male Asian vegetarians and female and male American vegetarians, respectively (38). These intakes produced negative balances of -0.5,-0.4, -1.0, and -1.1 mg Mn/day, respectively. The second study measured duplicate plate and bulk liquid collections of 15 adult men for 7 days (39). A negative balance of -0.7 mg Mn/day was seen on a daily intake of 4.28 mg. A third study also measured manganese balance for a one week period (40). The diet fed to 14 women contained 3.89 mg Mn/day either with and without a 20 mg iron supplement. The addition of the iron supplement changed manganese balance from a positive 0.44 mg/day to a negative -0.13 mg/day as determined from fecal excretion.

Balance Studies in Adults that Measured Integumental Losses

The only studies that have reported integumental losses of manganese have been done in our laboratory. In the first study (2), the integumental losses of men fed a semi-purified manganese deficient diet represented 13% of total body losses of manganese. After repletion with inorganic manganese for 10 days, the integumental losses decreased to 2.5% of total losses. This latter figure is similar to our second study which found integumental losses to range from 0.4 to 1.2% in men fed a conventional foods diet of varying manganese levels (Freeland-Graves et al. J. Nutr. Submitted for publication.) The highest percentage of integumental losses, 1.2%, was found with the lowest dietary level given. Thus integumental losses can be a significant route of excretion for manganese if intakes fall to very low levels. This suggests that the balances reported in studies that did not measure integumental losses may be more positive than is truely the case since output was underestimated.

In our first study described above (2), a negative balance of -0.02 mg Mn was found on a dietary level of 0.11 mg/day. This figure is small considering levels reported from past studies. However, the diet fed to the subjects was semi-purified, not whole foods. It is believed that retention of the mineral was enhanced by increased physiological needs caused by a manganese depletion from consumption of such a low dietary level. Furthermore, the diet did not contain any phytates and limited amounts of fiber.

In our second study, a diet of conventional foods was fed to five males, ages 19-20 years old, for 105 days. A baseline diet was supplemented with varying levels of inorganic manganese so that the total intake was 1.21, 2.06, 2.65, 2.89, and 3.79 mg Mn/day. Manganese balances were -0.09, -0.02, 0.14, -0.08, and 0.85 mg/day for these diets, respectively. Hair and nail losses have not been included in the integumental measurements in our laboratory or others. But the contribution of these losses to total obligatory losses has been calculated to be 0.74 µg/day (2). This small amount, 0.08% of total losses, would not significantly affect manganese balance.

Absorption and Retention

Studies of manganese requirements in humans are complicated by the fact that excretion, rather than absorption, is believed to be the major regulator of homeostatic control. Britton and Cotzias (41) fed diets containing varying levels of manganese to rats that had been injected with [54]Mn and found that the rate of excretion of the labeled tracer was linearly related to dietary concentrations of the mineral. However, other studies suggest that absorption may also play a regulating role under certain circumstances (42).

In balance studies, the re-excretion of absorbed manganese in the bile into the feces makes it difficult to isolate unabsorbed from endogenous (re-excreted) manganese. Thus, true absorption is difficult to determine. Furthermore, the excretion of manganese is highly variable between subjects and is dependent on the quantity given and the body status (43, 44). The variability of manganese absorption is shown in the study by Sandstrom et al. (44) in which individual rates of manganese absorption ranged from 1-7 to 14.5% in 14 subjects. When repeated several times, these rates were highly reproducible within the same individual. Whether these differences were due to variations in body status or dietary intakes is unknown.

When Thomson et al. (45) used an occulsive balloon to perfuse [54]Mn into the duodenum and proximal jejunum of eight subjects, the rate of absorption averaged 27% over a 1 hour period. Mena et al. (46) had previously found a lower rate of absorption, 3%, for orally administered [54]Mn by whole body counting for two weeks. However these authors felt that the measurements may have underestimated the amount actually absorbed since they could not account for the amount that had been absorbed and re-excreted.

North et al. (26) reported a retention rate of 41% with a mean intake of 3.7 mg Mn/day. This high retention rate was attributed to the fact that the young college women may still have been growing or due to incomplete collections since integumental losses were not measured. Lang et al. (27) found a similar retention rate, 47%, in subjects consuming 7.07 mg Mn/day. McLeod and Robinson (29) found a much lower rate of retention, 12% of intake, but were still puzzled why it was so high. The retention reported by these researchers, 0.32 mg/day, would approach the lower limit of total body stores of 12-20 mg (47) within 38 days. The higher retentions observed in older studies would saturate body stores even sooner. McLeod and Robinson suggested that failure to measure dermal and menstrual losses along with overestimation of intake might be contributing factors to the high retentions reported.

In contrast, Mena et al.(46) reported a 1.6% total body retention at 10 days following ingestion of $^{54}MnCl_2$. The retention was extrapolated to decline to 0.21 % of the ingested dose by 50 days. In children, the median retention rate for all studies was 12.6%. This value is slightly higher than the 8% retention reported by Mena in newborn receiving a 10 ug dose of $MnCl_2$ (48).

Factors Affecting the Human Requirement of Mn

A number of factors that may influence human requirements of manganese have been investigated in the literature. These factors include the iron status and age of the individual and dietary factors such as iron, calcium, phosphorus, phytates and fiber.

There are numerous studies that suggest a competitive interaction between manganese and iron (42). Mena et al. (46) reported that anemic subjects absorbed 7.5% of ingested manganese compared to 3.0% for normal subjects. Thomson et al. (45) also found that manganese absorption was increased in iron-deficient patients. When iron was added to a manganese-containing duodenal perfusate, the absorption of manganese was enhanced but the additional manganese was not retained. Kies et al. (40) found that the addition of 20 mg iron supplment to the diet of adult women caused negative manganese balance despite a dietary intake of 3.89 mg Mn/day.

Another human study involving an interaction between iron and manganese has recently been conducted in our laboratory (49). The presence of 40 mg dose of nonheme iron almost completely blocked the plasma uptake of a similar quantity of inorganic manganese. No such effect was seen with the same dose of heme iron.

A similar competition between iron and manganese has also been observed in rats. Gruden (50) found that iron added to the milk fed animals decreased tissue levels of manganese because of reduced intestinal absorption. However, this competition for absorption did not occur until the animal was old enough to develop mechanisms that regulate iron absorption. Similar age effects have been reported in humans. Mena (48) observed that the retention rates of manganese in premature infants, newborn, and adults declined from 15.6% to 8% to 1.6%, respectively. Overall, these studies suggest that both iron status and dietary form, as well as age, may influence human requirements for manganese.

Antagonist interactions have also been reported to occur between manganese and high dietary levels of calcium (Ca) and/or phosphorus. The relationship between manganese and calcium is particularly of concern because of the recent popularity of calcium supplements among women. Animal studies (51) have observed that a combination of excessive calcium and phosphorus in the diet intensify the need for manganese. However, Pond et al. (52) found no effect of varying dietary levels of either calcium or phosphorus on bone or tissue concentration of manganese in swine.

Two human studies have reported increased, but not significant, losses of fecal manganese in subjects when dietary levels of phosphorus were increased from 800 to 1,500 mg (30) and from 1,010 to 2,525 mg/day (31). In animals, elevated dietary levels of phosphorus have been reported to increase manganese requirements (51); however, the dietary level of calcium in this study was also high.

In a metabolic study of adolescent girls, Greger (31) suggested that the negative balances from diets containing 3.1 mg Ca/day may have been due to the high calcium level of the diet, 1,060 mg/day. However, Spencer et al. (30) found no effect of varying levels of calcium (200 to 1500 mg/day) on manganese balance in adult males. Similarly, Price et al. observed that manganese balance in preadolesent girls was unaffected by varying calcium from 260 to 620 g on high and low protein intakes (18) or by varying calcium from 300 to 1300 on high and low nitrogen intakes (19). The exception was a slight enhancement of balance by the addition of ammonium citrate on a low calcium intake; but this was negated by increasing dietary calcium.

In a study of five adults, our laboratory (Freeland-Graves et al., Trace Element Metabolism in Man and Animals. In press.) found that an oral dose of 800 mg of calcium significantly depressed the plasma uptake of 40 mg inorganic manganese. Whether or not this antagonistic relationship exists in normal food or diets is unclear.

The impact of a high fiber and high phytate diet on manganese bioavailability was illustrated in a metabolic balance study by Schwartz et al. (35). A mean negative manganese balance of -0.07 mg/day occurred despite a dietary manganese level of 13.9 mg/day. Excretion of phytate phosphorus was found to be significantly related to the excretion of manganese ($r = 0.86$). However, it is difficult to separate out the effect of the phytates from the fiber since both were present in high quantities.

The negative influence of fiber on manganese bioavailability has been shown by manganese tolerance tests in our laboratory (54). Both cellulose and pectin had an inhibitory influence on the plasma uptake of the mineral. Furthermore, excretion of manganese may also be affected by dietary fiber because of a report that the addition of pectin to a human diet increased fecal bile acid excretion by 33% (55). Since bile is the principle route of excretion for manganese (42), an increase in bile acid excretion would presumably also increase manganese excretion. Thus, it appears that diets high in either phytates or fiber or both may substantially increase the dietary requirement for manganese.

Dietary Levels and Sources of Manganese

Direct measurements of manganese in composite diets have been found to be 0.88 and 1.78 mg for summer and winter hospital menus, respectively (56); 2.3 mg in Japanese subjects (57); 2.7 mg (range of 0.8 to 7.1 mg) in New Zealand women (58); 3.0 mg in middle class U.S. men and women (37); 3.1 mg in U.S. adolescent girls (21); 3.2 mg in Canadian university meals (59); 3.3-5.5 mg in U. S. men (28); 4.6 mg in British diets (60); and 2.9 to 17.9 mg in Indian diets (61).

Gibson and Scythes (62) have reported both calculated intakes and direct analysis of 24 hr food composites in 100 Canadian women. The analyzed values of manganese were 121% higher than the calculated value of 3.1 mg/day. Although this mean value is within the range suggested by the Food and Nutrition Board (63), the intakes ranged from 0.7 to 10.8 mg/day and 37% had levels below the 2.5 mg level. The high intakes in this study (5 mg/day) were associated with frequent consumption of tea, a beverage which is high in manganese. Consumption of tea has also been reported to provide nearly half the manganese in the British diet (60).

Other significant food sources of manganese are nuts, seeds, and whole grains; leafy green vegetables are fair sources (56). Poor sources of manganese are meats, eggs, milk, sugar, and refined foods. A possible reason for some of the low manganese intakes that have been reported may be consumption of diets that are high in meat or refined foods. Kent and McCance (25) found that the dietary level of manganese was 8.7 mg/day when two subjects consumed diets that contained 40-50% of their energy from whole wheat flour. The substitution of a more refined white flour for the whole wheat reduced the manganese intake to 2.5 mg/day. Thus, the heavy reliance of western diets on meat, milk, sugary and refined foods, as well as fast foods, may lead to low dietary levels of manganese.

Recommended Allowance in Children and Adolescents

A daily manganese allowance of 1.25 mg/day for children, ages 6-10 years, was suggested by Engel et al. (17) based on a regression equation that calculated a value of 1.0 mg Mn needed for equilibrium. An additional allowance of 25% for growth and unmeasured losses increased the level to 1.25 mg. Schlage (64) reported that the average intakes were 1.4 mg/day for 3 to 5 year old children and 2.18 mg/day for 10-13 year olds. The current estimated safe and adequate daily dietary allowances for children are based on these studies. These range from 1.0 to 1.5 mg for ages 1-3, 1.5 to 2.0 mg for ages 4-6, and 2.0 to 3.0 mg for ages 7-10 (63). These values appear to include an adequate margain of safety.

In contrast, the estimated safe and adequate daily allowances for adolesents is 2.5-5.0 mg/day. In the only study of metabolic balance of manganese in adolesents (31), 13 of the 14 subjects were in negative balance while consuming diets containing 3.0 mg/day. Thus, the lower range of this recommendation for adolescents appears to be too low. However, the lack of other studies makes it difficult to provide a new recommendation.

Recommended Allowance in Adults

The current estimated safe and adequate allowance for manganese set by the Food and Nutrition Board for adults is 2.5-5 mg/day (63). The lower range of this figure was based on the study by McLeod and Robinson (29) in which equilibrium or excretion of manganese occured whenever the intake was 2.5 mg/day or higher. However, numerous studies (31-32, 34-40) have reported negative balances in subjects consuming mixed diets containing manganese levels ranging from 3.0 to 13.9 mg/day. These negative balances suggest that the lower limit of 2.5 mg for adults may also be too low.

A combination of all the data reported for manganese balances for adults in Table 1 is plotted against dietary intake in Fig. 1. Excluded were data determined by methods other than atomic absorption spectrophotometry and that from diets that were semi-purified or that contained more than 11 mg Mn/day. The regression equation calculated from these data is y = 0.185x - 0.657, in which y = balance and x = intake (r = 0.64, p<0.01). The point of theoretical manganese equilibrium is 3.55 mg/day. However, there are still a number of negative balances occurring above the theoretical point (34-36, 38, 40). Since the estimated safe and adequate daily dietary intake for manganese for adults is 2.5-5.0 mg (63), these negative balances suggest that the lower end of this range is too low. Our suggestions are for a lower limit of 3.5 mg/day for males. However, it should be recognized that intakes of 5 mg/day may be necessary to consistently acheive positive manganese balance if the diet is high in phytates, fiber, calcium, or iron.

The upper range of the recommended dietary level is open to speculation since toxicity has not been reported to occur from consumption of normal diets. In animals, toxicity does not occur until dietary levels reach 500-2000 ug/g (65). There is one report of an individual developing dementia from large doses of vitamins and minerals after 4-5 years (66). The second case of oral toxicity occurred in 16 subjects who drank well water that was contaminated with manganese from buried battteries (67). But the common cause of toxicity is industrial exposure via inhalation of fumes or dust which leads to a psychiatric disorder resembling schizophreniza. This is followed by a crippling neurological condition that is similar to Parkinson's disease (65). Since the toxicity level of manganese is so high and natural diets have been reported to contain up to 17.9 mg without any ill effects (60), our suggestion is to increase the upper limit to 7 mg.

In 1940, Basu and Malakar (22) first recommended a manganese requirement for adults to range from 3.7 to 5.5 mg/day, based on fecal excretions that were near positive balances. In 1949, De (23) calculated a lower requirement, 2.74 mg, using regression analysis of manganese balance. However, no diets were fed near this level. More recently, Rao and Rao have estimated adult requirements to be 3.72 mg (34) and 4.15 mg (33) per day based on consumption of Indian foods.

In our first metabolic study (2), mean obligatory losses of manganese were found to be 295 μg/day. Using these data, a minimal requirement for males, age 19-22, was calculated to be 0.74 mg Mn/day. This requirement is substantially less than that found in previous studies. However, this requirement was based on subjects consuming a semi-purified diet, not conventional foods. Furthermore, the subjects were consuming a manganese-deficient diet so that the obligatory losses were measured when the body was trying to conserve body stores of manganese. It seems reasonable that the addition of dietary factors which reduce bioavailability of the mineral coupled with a normal dietary intake of manganese would greatly increase the requirement. In our second study based on a diet of conventional foods, we found mean obligatory losses for the male subjects to be 392 μg/day. This higher figure is believed to be more characteristic of what occurs in everyday diets.

Currently, there are no recommendations for manganese requirements in pregnant and lactating women. In lactating women, Vuori et al. (68) have calculated that mothers would lose approximately 0.004 mg/day. This value is based on the third month of lactation with the loss of 950 ml of milk/day that contains 4.25 ug/liter. This additional 0.004 mg would not increase the manganese requirement. Information on additional needs of manganese during pregnancy is not available. Clearly, further investigations of the manganese requirements of humans are needed.

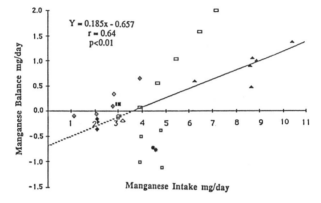

Figure 1. Manganese balance is plotted against dietary intake. The studies represented are ref. 29, (◇); ref. 30, (◆); ref. 31, (■); ref. 32, (Δ); ref. 33, (▲); ref. 34, (□); ref. 36, (•); ref. 37, (▯); ref. 38, (□); ref. 39 (*); and the present study (◈).

Is There a Problem in Meeting the Requirement ?

When 7-day diet composites were collected during the four seasons of the year, Patterson et al. (37) found a mean intake of 3.0 mg Mn/day and a nutrient density of 1.6 mg Mn/1000 kcal. Based on this figure, a consumption of 1560 kcal would be adequate to meet the lower limit of the suggested safe and adequate range (63). However, in Fig. 1 the theoretical point of equilibrium is 3.55 mg and it appears that approximately 5 mg is needed to consistently maintain positive balance. These would require a daily consumption of 2250 and 3125 Kcal, respectively. Thus, it seems plausible that some individuals may be at risk for being in negative manganese balance.

Conclusion

In the past, there was more concern about toxicity of manganese from industrial exposure than deficiencies. Also, dietary intakes were higher when whole grains were an essential component of diets. But the larger proportion of meats and refined foods in current diets may lead to low dietary intakes. In view of the fact that numerous studies have reported negative manganese balances on conventional diets and manganese deficiency has been implicated as producing osteoporotic bone changes, it would seem prudent for individuals, particularly women, to increase their dietary intake. A suggested range of intake is 3.5-7 mg; however this lower limit may be insufficient to produce positive balance when special diets are consumed.

Acknowledgment

This work was supported in part by USDA grant #84-CRCR-1-1497.

Literature Cited

1. Doisy, E.A. Jr. In Trace Substances in Environmental Health; Hemphill, D., Ed.; University of Missouri: Columbia, 1972; Vol. 6, p 193-99.
2. Friedman, B. J.; Freeland-Graves, J. H.; Bales, C. W.; Behmardi, F.; Shorey-Kutschke, R. L.; Willis, R. A.; Crosby, J. B.; Tricket, P. C.; Houston, S. D. J. Nutr., 1987, 117, 133-43.
3. Leach, R. M. Jr. Fed. Proc. 1971, 30, 991-4.
4. Myara, I.; Charpentier, C; Lemmonier, A. Life Sci. 1984, 134, 1985-988.
5. Krishna, G.; Whitlock, W. Jr.; Feldbreugge, D. H.; Proter, J. W. Arch. Biochem. Biophysics 1966, 114, 200-15.
6. Strause, L. G.; Hegenauer, J.; Saltman, P.; Cone, R.; Resnick, D. J. Nutr. 1986, 116, 134-41.
7. Hurry, V. J.; Gibson, R. S. Biol. Trace Elem. Res. 1982, 4, 157-73.
8. Alexander, F. W.; Clayton, B. E.; Delves, H. T. Quart. J. Med.1974, 53, 89-111.
9. Aggett, P. J.; Thorn, J. M.; Delves, H. T.; Harries, J. T.; Clayton, B. D. Monogr. Paediat. 1979, 10, 8-11.
10. Tanaka, Y. J. Am. Coll. Nutr. 1982, 1, 113.
11. Papavasiliou, P. S.; Kutt, H.; Miller, S. T.; Rosal, V.; Wang, Y. Y.; Aronson, R. B.Neurology 1979, 29, 1466-73.
12. Carl, G. F.; Keen, C. L.; Gallagher, B. B.; Clegg, M. S.; Littleton, W. H.; Flannery, D. B.; Hurley, L. S. Neurology 1986, 36, 1584-87.
13. Cotzias, G. C.; Papavasiliou, P. S.; Hughes, E. R.; Tang, L.; Borg., D. C. J. Clin. Invest. 1968, 47, 992-1001.

14. Comens, P. Am. J. Med. 1956, 20, 944-45.
15. Hurley, L. S.; Wooley, D. E.; Rosenthal, F.; Timiras, P. S. Am. J. Physiol. 1963, 204, 493-96.
16. Everson, G. J.; Daniels, A. L. J. Nutr. 1934, 8, 497-502.
17. Engel, R. W.; Price, N. O.; Miller, R. F. J. Nutr. 1967, 92, 197-204.
18. Price, N. O.; Bunce, G. E.; Engel, R. W. Am. J. Clin. Nutr. 1970, 23, 258-60.
19. Price, N. O.; Bunce, G. E. Nutr. Rep. Intl. 1972, 5, 275-80.
20. Widdowson, E. M. In Mineral Metabolism in Pediatrics; Barltrop, P, Ed; Oxford: Blackwell Scientific, 1969; Chap.6.
21. Greger, J. L.; Baligar, P.; Abernathy, R. P.; Bennett, O. A.; Peterson, T. Am. J. Clin. Nutr. 1978, 31, 117-21.
22. Basu, K. P.; Malakar. Ind. Chem. Soc. 1940, 17, 317-25.
23. De, H. N.; Basu, K. P. Ind. J. Med. Res. 1949, 37, 213.
24. De, H. N. Ind. J. Med. Res. 1949, 37, 301-8.
25. Kent, N. L.; McCance, R. A. Biochem. J. 1941, 35, 877-82.
26. North, B.B.; Leichsenring, J. M.; Norris, L. M. J. Nutr. 1960, 72, 217-23.
27. Lang, V. M.; North, B. B.; Morse, L. M. J. Nutr. 1965, 85, 132-38.
28. Tipton, I. H.; Stewart, P. L.; Dickson, J. Hlth. Phy. 1969, 16, 455-62.
29. McLeod, B. E.; Robinson, M. F. Br. J. Nutr. 1972, 27, 221-27.
30. Spencer, H.; Asmussen, C. R.; Holtzman, R. B.; Kramer, L. Am. J. Clin. Nutr. 1979, 32, 1867-75.
31. Greger, J. L.; Snedeker, S. M. J. Nutr. 1980, 110, 22, 43-53.
32. Johnson, M. A.; Baier, M. J.; Greger, J. L. Am. J. Clin. Nutr. 1982, 35, 1332-38.
33. Rao, C. N.; Rao, B.S. Nutr. Metab. 1980, 24, 244-54.
34. Rao, C. N.; Rao, B.S. Nutr. Repts. Intl. 1982, 26, 1113-21.
35. Schwartz, R.; Apgar, B. J.; Wien. E. M. Am. J. Clin. Nutr. 1986, 43, 444-55.
36. Hill, A. D.; Morris, E. R.; Ellis, R.; Cottrell, S.; Steele, P.; Moy, T.; Moser, P. B. Fed Proc. 1984, 43, 683.
37. Patterson, K. Y.; Holbrook, J. T.; Bodner, J. E.; Kelsay, J. L. Smith Jr., J. C.; Veillon, C. Am. J. Clin. Nutr. 1984, 40, 1397-403.
38. Kelsay, J. L.; Clark, W. M.; Frazier, C. W.; Prather, E. S. Fed. Proc. 1985, 44, 757.
39. Hill, A. D., Morris, E. R.; Ellis, R.; Moy, T.; Moser, P. B. Fed. Proc. 1986, 45, 375.
40. Kies, C.; Creps, C.; Kowalski, C.; Fox, H. M. Fed. Proc. 1985, 44, 1850.
41. Britton, A. A. ; Cotzias, G. C.: Am. J. Physiol. 1966, 211, 203-6.
42. Keen, C. L.; Lonnerdal, B.; Hurley, L. S. In Biochemistry of the Essential Ultratrace Elements; Frieden, E., Ed.; Plenum: New York, 1984; Chap. 5.
43. Mahoney, J. P.; Small, W. J. J. Clin. Invest. 1968, 47, 643-53.
44. Sandstrom, Y.; Davidson, L.; Cederblad, A.; Lonnerdal, B. Fed. Proc. 1987, 46, 570.
45. Thomson, A. B.; Olatunbosun, D.; Valberg, L. S. J. Lab. Clin. Med. 1971, 78, 642-55.
46. Mena, I.; Horuchi, K.; Burke, K.; Cortzias, G. C. Neurology 1969, 19, 1000-6.
47. Cotzias, G. C. Physiol. Rev., 1958, 38, 503-32.
48. Mena, I. In Metals in the Environment; Waldron, H. A., Ed.; Academic: New York, 1980; Chap. 7.
49. Freeland-Graves, J. H.; Lin, P. -H.; Dougherty, V.; Bales, C. First Meeting Intl. Soc. Trace Elem. Res. Hum. 1986, 56.
50. Gruden, N. Nutr. Repts. Intl. 1984, 30, 553-57.

51. Hawkins, G. E. Jr; Wise, G. H.; Matrone, G.; Waugh, R. K.; Lott, W. L. J. Dairy Sci. 1955, 38, 536-47.
52. Pond, W. G.; Walker, E. F. Jr.; Kirtland, D. J. Anim. Sci. 1978, 46, 686-91.
53. Davies, N.T.; Nightingale, R. Br. J. Nutr. 1975, 34, 243-58.
54. Bales, C. W.; Freeland-Graves, J. H.; Lin, P.-H.; Stone, J. M.; Dougherty, V. In Nutritional Bioavailability of Manganese; Kies, C., Ed.; American Chemical Society: Washington, D.C., 1987.
55. Kay, R. M.; Truswell, A. S. Am. J. Clin. Nutr. 1977, 30, 171-75.
56. Gormican, A. J. Am. Dietet. Assoc. 1970, 56, 397-403.
57. Yamagata, N. ; Yamagata, T. Bull. Inst. Publ. Hlth. 1964, 13, 11.
58. Guthrie, B. E.; Robinson, M. F. Br. J. Nutr. 1977, 38, 55-63.
59. Srivastava, U.; Makhija, S. L.; Nadeau, M.; Rakshit, A. K; Carbonneau, N.; Guennou, L.; Khare, I. Nutr. Repts. Intl. 1981, 24, 1139-51.
60. Wenlock, R. W.; Buss, D. H.; Dixon, E. J. Br. J. Nutr. 1979, 41, 253-61.
61. Rao, C. N.; Rao, B.S. Ind. J. Med. Res. 1981, 73, 904-9.
62. Gibson, R. S.; Scythes, C. A. Br. J. Nutr. 1982, 48, 241-8.
63. Recommended Dietary Allowances, National Academy of Sciences, 1980, 9th ed.
64. Schlage, C. Med. Ernahr. 1972, 13, 49-54.
65. Underwood, E. J. Trace Elements in Human and Animal Nutrition; 4th Ed.; Academic: New York, 1977; Chap. 7.
66. Banta, G.; Markesbery, W. R. Neurology 1977, 27, 213-16.
67. Kawamura, R.; Ikuta, H.; Fukuzami, T. Jpn. J. Bacteriol. 1940, 537, 687-710.
68. Vuori, E.; Makinen, S. M.; Kara, R.; Kuitunen, P. Am. J. Clin. Nutr. 1980, 33, 227-31.

RECEIVED December 1, 1986

Chapter 10

Manganese Metabolism in Epilepsy: Normal or Abnormal?

G. F. Carl[1-4], Carl L. Keen[5], B. B. Gallagher[1], and L. S. Hurley[5]

[1]Department of Neurology, Medical College of Georgia, Augusta, GA 30912
[2]Department of Medicine, Medical College of Georgia, Augusta, GA 30912
[3]Department of Psychiatry, Medical College of Georgia, Augusta, GA 30912
[4]Medical Research Service, Veterans Administration Medical Center, Augusta, GA 30910
[5]Department of Nutrition, University of California—Davis, Davis, CA 95616

There is a relationship between manganese and epilespy that remains undefined. While animal experiments have shown that manganese deficiency increases seizure susceptibility, clinical work has established that mean whole blood manganese concentration is significantly lower in an epileptic population than it is in a control population. One suggestion has been that the lower blood manganese concentration in epileptics is due to seizure activity. Alternatively, others have suggested a possible genetic origin of the lower manganese levels in a subgroup of epileptics. It has also been reported that soft tissue manganese levels are responsive to adrenal steroids, and it is known that some epileptics with a temporal lobe focus exhibit abnormal pituitary/adrenal control suggesting a possible hormonal cause for the lower blood manganese levels.

In 1961 Hurley and coworkers ([1]) observed that congenitally ataxic rats were more susceptible to seizures induced by electroshock than were controls. This report followed closely a publication of preliminary findings ([2]) indicating that seizures induced in rats by hydralazine injection could be prevented by prior injection of manganese chloride. These preliminary findings were later confirmed ([3]) and indeed it was shown that it was the manganese deficiency that increased the seizure susceptibility of the rats independent of the ataxia ([3]).

The first report of abnormal manganese concentrations in human epileptics was published in 1967 and indicated high serum manganese concentrations in epileptics compared to non-epileptic controls ([4]). The authors were apparently unaware of the previous animal work that demonstrated a link between manganese deficiency and increased susceptibility to seizure. It was not until 1978 that Tanaka ([5]) presented data indicating that whole blood manganese concentrations were lower in epileptic children than in control children of similar age. A year later Papavasiliou and coworkers ([6]) in a study of 52

0097–6156/87/0354–0105$06.00/0
© 1987 American Chemical Society

adult epileptic patients found that the patients had a mean whole blood manganese concentration that was 76% that of 24 controls (p < 0.002). They examined their data for correlations between manganese levels and either serum anticonvulsant concentrations or seizure frequency. While they found no relationship between blood manganese and medication, seizure frequency did show a significant (p < 0.001) relationship to blood manganese concentration by analysis of variance. These investigators also did a limited study into the possibility that there is a genetic lesion underlying the lower blood manganese concentrations observed in some epileptics. In their study the whole blood manganese concentrations in six non-epileptic relatives of epileptic patients were normal relative to those in the control population. Unfortunately, these relatives were not further identified, so that it remains unknown to which patients they were related or whether or not they were related to the same or different patients. Interestingly, these investigators also measured manganese concentration in the hair of patients and controls. Although the mean manganese concentration in patients' hair was lower than that of controls, the difference was not statistically significant due to the variability in the hair manganese measurements. In addition, they found no significant correlation between hair manganese and blood manganese concentrations.

In 1980 Hoffman (7) reported that serum manganese concentrations were the same in epileptics and non-epileptic controls in populations of both adults and children. This observation suggests that the differences reported by Tanaka (5) and by Papavasiliou, et al. (6) in whole blood were due to differences in manganese concentrations in the blood cells, probably erythrocytes. Whether this apparent deficiency in the erythrocytes of some epileptics translates into lower manganese concentrations in other tissues of these epileptics is unknown.

To further examine the relationship between blood Mn concentration and seizure frequency, Papavasiliou and Miller (8) injected mice with ^{54}Mn at various times before and after inducing a seizure by either maximal electroshock or pentylene tetrazole injection. They followed the distribution of the radioactive manganese in the tissues of the mice and found that ^{54}Mn injected immediately after the siezure was taken up more readily by the liver (67% increase) and less readily by brain (53% decrease) and carcass (42% decrease) than ^{54}Mn injected either into sham-seized mice or into mice before induction of a seizure. They also found that chronic electroshock-induced seizure activity in mice (2/day, 6 day/wk, 3 wk) resulted in a decrease in brain manganese concentration (16%) and an increase in liver manganese concentration (67%) compared to sham-treated controls. These data were interpreted as indicating that the large energy demand of the seizure causes a shift of manganese, which is important in energy metabolism, from other tissues (such as erythrocytes and brain) into the liver. They argue that reequilibration of the manganese takes time, and intervening seizures further shift the manganese toward the liver. Consequently, whole blood manganese concentration (as well as manganese concentration in other non-hepatic tissues) decreases as seizure frequency increases.

A recent study from our laboratory using age, sex, race and weight matched controls with blinded analyses confirmed previous reports of low concentrations of manganese in whole blood of epileptics (11.8 ppb vs. 8.3 ppb,p < 0.001) (9). We also confirmed the lack of a correlation between anticonvulsant medication and whole blood manganese levels, either as a function of total medication (Figure 1) or individual anticonvulsants (Table I), but were unable to confirm correlation between seizure frequency and blood manganese concentration (Figure 2). However, we did report that epileptics with seizures of unknown etiology had significantly lower blood manganese concentrations than epileptics whose seizures could reasonably be attributed to injury or disease. We suggested that a subgroup of epileptics may exhibit low blood manganese levels of genetic origin. We also examined plasma zinc and copper concentrations in our patients and in controls and found no differences (Table II) indicating that the lower manganese levels are not a sign of a generalized trace element deficiency. This finding contributes to the controversy involving copper and zinc concentrations in the blood of epileptics which has been reviewed in one of the most recent reports on this subject (10).

Table I.   Correlation Between Whole Blood Manganese
Concentration and Plasma Anticonvulsant
Concentrations in Epileptic Patients

Drug	N	Slope	Intercept	Correlation Coefficient
Phenytoin	23	+0.149	6.25	0.291
Phenobarbital	16	−0.012	7.40	−0.037
Primidone	13	+0.011	6.25	0.017
Carbamazepine	26	−0.024	8.72	−0.020
Valproate	9	+0.056	7.78	0.182

Manganese concentrations were measured by atomic absorption spectrophotometry and anticonvulsant concentrations by EMIT (Syva, Palo Alto. CA). Linear regression analyses indicate no significant correlation between manganese concentration and any anticonvulsant concentration.

It is interesting to note that glucocorticoids have been shown to affect the distribution of manganese in the body of the mouse (11,12). Seizures have also been shown to affect manganese distribution in mice (8), and, in temporal lobe epileptics, the control of the glucocorticoid output from the adrenal gland is apparently abnormal (13). Just how these independent observations might be related is not clear. When mice were treated with ACTH, cortisol or prednisolone, manganese showed a redistribution from the liver to the carcass (11,12). However, adrenalectomy did not have the opposite effect, unless extremely high doses of manganese were given (12). But, as described above, seizures apparently caused a redistribution of manganese in the opposite direction, from the carcass to the liver (8). This would indicate that the seizures do not

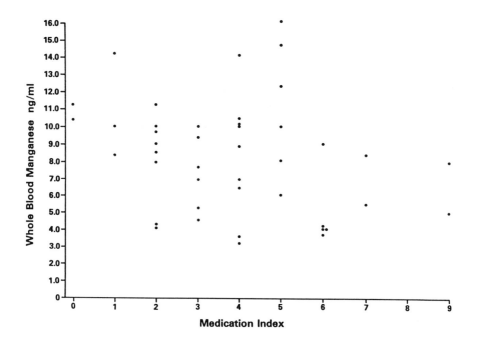

Figure 1.   Whole blood manganese levels in epileptic patients
vs. medication index.   Whole blood manganese was measured by
atomic absorption spectrophotometry.   The medication index is a
composite measure of anticonvulsant concentrations in plasma as
a relationship of each anticonvulsant to its therapeutic range.
The medication index increases as a function of the relative
concentration of each anticonvulsant and as a sum of all anticonvulsant concentrations.   There was no correlation between
whole blood manganese and medication index (r = −0.236.)

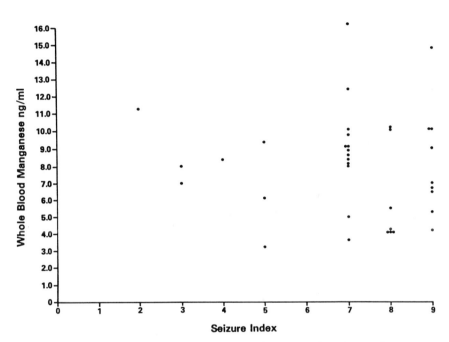

Figure 2.   Whole blood manganese levels in epileptic patients
vs. seizure index.   Whole blood manganese was measured by atomic
absorption spectrophotometry.   Seizure index is a linearized
measure of seizure frequency.   There was no correlation between
blood manganese concentration and seizure index (r = -0.067).

Table II. Comparison of Plasma Zinc and Plasma Copper Concentra-
          tions Between Epileptics and Age, Sex, Race and
          Height/Weight Ratio Matched Controls

	Epileptics N = 44	Controls N = 44
Copper (µg/ml)	1.12±0.28	1.13±0.37
Zinc (µg/ml)	0.59±0.15	0.62±0.36

Zinc and copper values are expressed as mean ± S.D. Zinc and copper
were measured using flame atomic absorption spectrophotometry. A
two tailed t-test was used to compare the means for copper (p = 0.8)
and for zinc (p = 0.6).

cause an increase in glucocorticoids. However, in patients whose
seizures originate in the temporal lobe, there is an increased
secretion of both ACTH and cortisol and the former, at least, does
not seem to be drug induced (13). In addition, surgical removal of
the seizure focus from the temporal lobe allows ACTH and cortisol
secretion to return to normal whether or not the seizures are controlled. It is unknown at this time what effect the surgical
reduction of seizures might have on the distribution of manganese in
these patients or whether there is any relationship between glucocorticoids and manganese distribution in humans.

While a relationship between epilepsy and blood manganese
concentration has been established, the nature of the relationship
is unclear. It is evident that considerable work needs to be done
to examine the mechanisms involved in this relationship. In our
opinion, the effects and efficacy of manganese supplementation in
epileptic patients with low blood manganese need to be investigated.
Keen and coworkers (14,15) have shown that in rats whole blood
manganese concentration is a reflection of the relative levels of
manganese in soft tissues. If this is true in epileptic patients
with low blood manganese, then low concentrations of manganese can
be expected in the tissues of these patients. This possibility
needs to be investigated.

Interestingly manganese toxicity is manifested initially in the
central nervous system, generally with the induction of behavioral
changes or Parkinsonian-like symptoms (16). Whether there is a
relationship between this observation and the deficiency of manganese in some epileptics is a matter for speculation, but the limbic
system seems to be involved in both the behavioral effects of
manganese toxicity, and the manganese-deficiency-related epileptic
seizures, at least those of the temporal lobe that result in increased ACTH and cortisol levels (13). However, the structures of
the temporal lobe apparently have manganese concentrations not
significantly different from other parts of the brain (17).

One point that is abundantly clear about the relationship between manganese and epilepsy is that much remains to be learned.

Acknowledgements

The authors wish to express their gratitude for support from the Department of Nutrition of the University of California at Davis and the Department of Neurology of the Medical College of Georgia and the Medical Research Service of the Veterans Administration.

Literature Cited

1. Hurley, L. S.; Woolley, D. E.; Timiras, P. S. Proc. Soc. Exptl. Biol. Med. 1961, 106, 343-46.
2. Comens, P. In Metal-Binding in Medicine; Seven, M. J.; Johnson, L. A., Eds., Lippincott: Philadelphia, 1960; p 312.
3. Hurley, L. S.; Woolley, D. E.; Rosenthal, F.; Timiras, P. S. Am. J. Physiol. 1963, 204, 493-96.
4. Mindadse, A. A.; Tschikowani, T. I. Dtsch. Gesundheitsw. 1967, 22, 1746-48.
5. Tanaka, Y.; Presented at the American Chemical Society National Meeting, Chicago, 1978.
6. Papavasiliou, P. S.; Kutt, H.; Miller, S. T.; Rosal, V.; Wang, Y. Y.; Aronson, R. B. Neurology 1979, 29, 1466-73.
7. Hoffman, H. Klin. Wochenschr. 1980, 58, 157-58.
8. Papavasiliou, P. S.; Miller, S. T. Exptl. Neurol. 1983, 82, 223-36.
9. Carl, G. F.; Keen, C. L.; Gallagher, B. B.; Clegg, M. S.; Littleton, W. H.; Flannery, D. B.; Hurley, L.S. Neurology 1986, 36, 1584-87.
10. Taylor, A.; Glose, K. Human Toxicol., 1986, 5, 195-200.
11. Hughes, E. R.; Cotzias, G. C. Am. J. Physiol. 1961, 201, 1061-64.
12. Hughes, E. R.; Miller, S. T.; Cotzias, G. C. Am. J. Physiol. 1966, 211, 207-10.
13. Gallagher, B. B.; Murvin, A.; Flanigin, H. F.; King, D. W.; Luney, D. Epilepsia 1984, 25, 683-89.
14. Keen, C L.; Clegg, M. S.; Lonnerdal, B.; Hurley, L. S. N. Eng. J. Med. 1983, 308, 1230.
15. Clegg, M. S.; Lonnerdal, B.; Hurley, L. S.; Keen, C. L. Anal. Biochem. 1986, 157, 12-18.
16. Keen, C. L.; Lonnerdal, B; Hurley, L. S. In Biochemistry of the Essential Ultratrace Elements; Frieden, E., Ed.; Plenum: New York, 1984; pp 89-132.
17. Bonilla, E.; Salazar, E.; Villasmil, J. J.; Villalobos, R. Neurochem. Res. 1982, 7, 221-27.

RECEIVED May 11, 1987

Chapter 11

Plasma Uptake of Manganese
Influence of Dietary Factors

Connie W. Bales[1], Jeanne H. Freeland-Graves, Pao-Hwa Lin, Jan M. Stone, and Virginia Dougherty

Division of Nutrition, University of Texas at Austin, Austin, TX 78712

The influence of three dietary factors - pectin, cellulose and phytates - on plasma uptake of manganese (Mn) was studied in adults administered Mn tolerance tests. Plasma samples were collected at hourly intervals following administration of various doses of several Mn salts. It was found that a 40 to 50 mg dose of elemental Mn was necessary to produce consistent plasma responses and that manganese chloride ($MnCl_2$) was better absorbed than the sulfate or acetate form. In fasting subjects, plasma Mn was 0.64, 1.29, 1.12, 0.95, and 0.75 ug/L at hours 0, 1, 2, 3, and 4, respectively, following a 40 mg Mn dose provided as $MnCl_2$. Uptake of Mn chloride was markedly reduced by 15 g high-methoxyl pectin, and to a lesser extent by both 15 g alpha cellulose and 300 mg sodium phytate.

Manganese is an essential nutrient for humans with a daily estimated adequate safe and daily dietary intake of 2.5 to 5.0 mg (1). Yet trace mineral nutriture depends not only upon dietary intake, but also upon availability for absorption. Currently, little is known regarding the influence of dietary factors on the absorption of manganese. Thus the intent of these studies was to (a) develop a test that would readily measure Mn bioavailability in humans and (b) utilize this test to determine the influences of various dietary factors on Mn bioavailability.

Absorption of Manganese in Adults

Understanding of manganese bioavailability is limited by a paucity of information concerning the mechanism of its absorption in humans. Although the proportion of oral manganese which is

[1]Current address: Center for the Study of Aging and Human Development, Box 3003, Duke University, Durham, NC 27710

absorbed from the gut is reported to be as low as 3 to 4% (2), the scarcity of data in healthy subjects prevents clear definition of the rate of manganese absorption. Using whole body counting of ^{54}MnCl$_2$, Mena et al. (3) found a 3.0 ± 0.5% rate of absorption in 11 subjects; however, manganese reabsorbed into the enterohepatic circulation was not taken into account in this study. Thus the rate of manganese absorption may have been underestimated. A much higher absorption rate was reported by Thomson et al. (4) who examined uptake of ^{54}MnCl$_2$ in segments of duodenum and jejunum using a double-lumen tube. A mean absorption rate of 27 ± 3% was found for the eight subjects measured.

Manganese appears to be absorbed throughout the small bowel, although the exact site of maximum uptake in humans has not been conclusively determined. Animal studies indicate that absorption is more rapid in the duodenum and jejunum than the ileum (4,5) and that manganese is most likely absorbed in the divalent form (6). When Garcia-Aranda et al. (5) studied intestinal uptake of manganese in adult rats, the absorptive process was found to be rapidly saturated, suggesting a transport mechanism with a strong affinity but a low capacity for the mineral.

Biliary excretion provides the major route for manganese homeostatic control (7-9); this mechanism is apparently essential when intakes are high (10). However, there is evidence that absorption can also play a role in the manganese homeostasis in cattle (11, 12) and rats (10,13).

Plasma uptake of manganese

A series of experiments were initiated to examine the effects of dietary fibers on the plasma uptake of an oral dose of manganese in humans. Stable isotope techniques are the ideal methods for measuring the intestinal absorption of minerals; however this technique is impossible for manganese because of its monoisotopic nature (14). Also, ethical considerations prohibit the use of radioactive forms of manganese. Thus, a technique which was both relatively easy to conduct and safe to administer repeatedly to the same subject was developed.

The manganese tolerance test measures the plasma uptake of pharmacological doses of manganese. This test is analogous to the plasma tolerance test for zinc, which was described in 1973 (15) and has subsequently been used extensively in this (16) and other laboratories as a qualitative indicator of absorption (17,18).

In manganese tolerance tests, blood samples are collected at fasting and at regular time intervals following administration of an oral manganese load. In this study, results of tolerance tests with manganese alone were subsequently compared with plasma responses in the same subjects when the manganese dose was accompanied by various dietary components.

Development of the Protocol. Reported concentrations of plasma manganese vary considerably according to sample preparation and method of analysis. Although plasma levels as high as 34.30 ug/L have been reported, concentrations in the range of 0.5 to 1.2 ug/L are generally considered most accurate (19). In this study, fasting levels of manganese were measured on several occasions in the same

healthy adult subjects. Mean concentration of plasma manganese was
found to be 0.62 ± 0.18 ug/L. As shown in Figure 1, inter-subject
variation appears to be more prevalent than intra-subject variance.
Similarly, Cotzias et al. (20) reported significant variance in
plasma manganese among subjects but little within-subject variation.
However, statistical analysis of our data indicated no significant
differences among or within individuals.

The initial plasma uptake tests were used to select a readily
absorbable salt form of manganese since differences in bioavailability have been reported for various salts of other minerals
(18,21). In animal studies, most reports have indicated that a
variety of chemical forms of manganese are equally well absorbed and
retained. Yet results have varied according to the type of salt
used and the criteria used for assessing bioavailability (22-26).
Henning et al. (27) found that $MnCl_2$ was retained in the bodies of
chicks to a greater extent than was either MnO_2 or $MnSO_4$. However,
when these two salts were fed in excess, Southern and Baker (26)
found little difference in their relative bioavailability. In this
study, three forms of manganese were tested for plasma uptake: the
chloride, sulfate, and acetate salts. In most subjects, response to
a 50 mg dose of the chloride salt was better than the sulfate or
acetate form (Figure 2). Thus $MnCl_2$ was the salt used for all
subsequent tolerance tests.

The manganese load in the tolerance tests was administered in
capsule form along with 200 ml of deionized distilled water.
Subjects were not allowed to eat or drink anything else during the
test period. Samples of plasma were collected after a 12-hour fast
and hourly for 4 hours postdose. Plasma samples were analyzed for
manganese content using graphite furnace atomic absorption spectrophotometry (Friedman, et al., J. Nutr. In press.) Consecutive tests
in the same subjects were separated by a minimum of 14 days, since
preliminary testing indicated no residual effect of the manganese
dose after this time interval.

As expected, the plasma response was more consistent and
significantly higher when the oral dose was increased. Although
every effort was made to keep the manganese load as low as possible,
doses providing less than 40 mg elemental manganese as $MnCl_2$ did not
produce consistent plasma responses in all subjects. Thus the 40 mg
dose was chosen as the baseline load for most tests; it was found to
give a consistent plasma response but less gastric discomfort than
the 50 mg dose.

Results of Baseline Tests. Figure 3 presents the effect on fasting
levels of manganese when the standard oral dose of 40 mg elemental
manganese (as 144 mg $MnCl_2$) was ingested by 11 subjects who later
participated in bioavailability testing. The five female and six
male subjects were of normal height for weight, with a mean age of
27 ± 4 years. These subjects were in good health and had not used
supplements of manganese prior to the study.

The heavy line in Figure 3 represents the mean curve (n=11) for
the change in plasma manganese and the other lines show the typical
plasma responses of individual subjects (n=5). The mean increase in
plasma manganese peaked at hour 1, at approximately 103% above
fasting. The mean concentrations of plasma manganese were 0.64,
1.29, 1.12, 0.94 and 0.75 ug/L at hours 0,1,2,3, and 4 postdose,

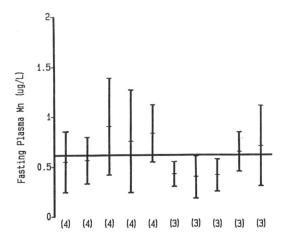

Figure 1. Variation in fasting concentrations of plasma manganese within and among normal subjects (n=11). Number in parentheses indicates the number of measurements made on the same individual. Straight line indicates mean value for the group.

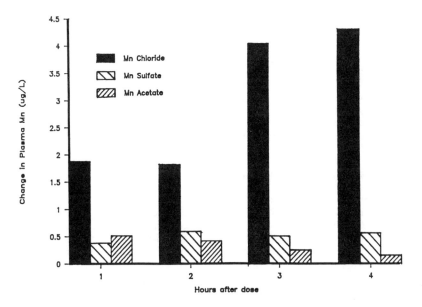

Figure 2. Typical plasma response to 50 mg of manganese provided in the chloride, sulfate, or acetate form.

respectively. Although responses were variable among subjects, plasma levels generally peaked at hours one or two postdose and were close to fasting levels by hour 4. This rapid clearance of manganese from blood has also been observed with injected doses (12,28).

Influence of Dietary Factors on Plasma Uptake of Manganese

Once the test had been developed and standardized in the subjects, the influence of dietary fibers on manganese uptake was studied. Fiber was examined since diets providing large amounts have been suggested to play a preventative role for a variety of disease states, including diabetes, and diseases of the large bowel and cardiovascular system (29,30). However, fiber has also been reported to have a possible detrimental impact on the bioavailability of some minerals including zinc (31-33), copper (31), calcium (33,34), iron (35) and magnesium (33,36).

Only a limited number of studies have investigated the relationship of fiber and manganese. In 1986, Halpin and Baker (37) fed casein-dextrose diets supplemented with wheat bran or a corn-soybean meal mixture for 7 weeks and found that both diets impaired growth and depressed tissue concentrations of Mn. In a study of human subjects fed diets containing bran fiber and phytate, Schwartz et al. (38) found negative or only slightly positive manganese balances, despite manganese intakes (13.9-17.7 mg/day) that were well above the recommended levels (1). Possible reasons for the detrimental influence of fiber on mineral bioavailability may be the formation of mineral-fiber chelates in the gastrointestinal tract, dilution with extra water, and/or decreased transit time (39).

Since almost nothing is known about the effect of isolated fibers on the absorption of manganese and constituents of dietary fiber vary both in chemical and physical properties, the effects of two major types of fiber -- cellulose and pectin -- were examined using our protocol. The effect of phytate was also measured since it is associated with high fiber foods and has been reported to increase requirements for manganese (40).

Cellulose. Fiber components differ in their ability to bind to bile (41), the primary route of excretion of manganese (9). Cellulose, the most abundant natural fiber, has been studied for its potential effects on bile and lipid metabolism (42). It is naturally present in high fiber diets and is also commonly added to many commercially-produced food products. Previous studies have shown cellulose to decrease intestinal uptake of a variety of minerals, including zinc, phosphorus, calcium, magnesium, and iron (32,43,44). In many cases, however, the effect of cellulose has not been considered to be anti-nutritional (32). It has been generally believed that cellulose has a lower binding affinity for minerals than other constituents of dietary fiber (33,45).

In order to determine the independent effect of cellulose on manganese bioavailability, manganese tolerance tests were administered with 15 g of alpha cellulose (Sigma Co., Inc., St. Louis, MO) to six human subjects. The cellulose was given in gelatin capsules in addition to a 40 mg dose of manganese as $MnCl_2$ and 200 ml of deionized water. As seen in Figure 4, the addition of cellulose to

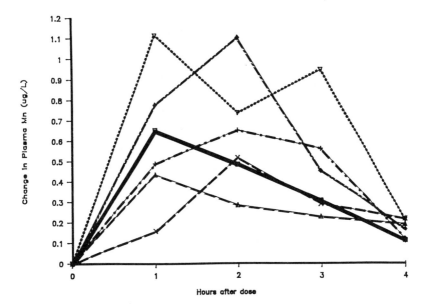

Figure 3: Mean plasma uptake of 40 mg manganese as $MnCl_2$ is shown as dark line (n=10). The other five curves illustrate typical manganese uptake in individual subjects.

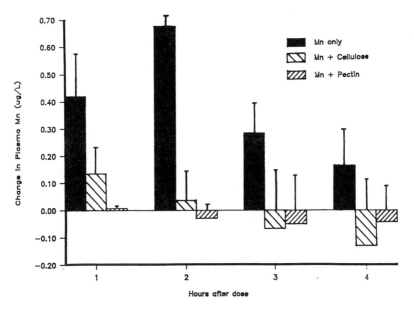

Figure 4: Effect of 15g cellulose or high-methoxyl pectin on plasma uptake of 40 mg manganese (n=6).

a manganese dose caused a reduction in plasma uptake of manganese.
This tendency was noted throughout the test, but was significant
only at the second hour postdose.

It is possible that the effect of purified cellulose on manganese differs from that of cellulose provided from whole foods.
Ranhotra et al. (46) found that products naturally high in cellulose
such as wheat bran, soy flour, and vegetable flour reduced availability of iron, while purified cellulose had no effect. Further
studies with cellulose in both purified and natural form will be
necessary to determine if the reduction in manganese uptake produced
by cellulose could lead to adverse nutritional consequences.

Pectin. Pectic substances are a complex group of indigestible
polysaccharides that are classified as fiber. Although the nutritional and physiological effects of pectins have been previously
noted (47,48), the diversity of their structure and chemistry has
complicated research concerning their effects on mineral bioavailability. It is known that pectins bind polyvalent metals including
magnesium, calcium, and iron (47). However, the physiological
significance of this phenomenon may be determined by the type and
dose of pectin and the subjects under study. For example, Sandberg
et al. (49) showed that 15 g of citrus pectin reduced apparent
absorption of iron, but not of calcium, phosphorous, magnesium, and
zinc in ileostomy patients. Likewise, Monnier et al. (50) demonstrated that pectin caused a decrease in iron absorption in patients
with idiopathic hemochromatosis.

Although little is known about the effects of pectins on the
absorption of manganese, administration of pectin has been shown to
increase the excretion of bile acids in humans (48). In the only
previous study related to the influence of pectin on manganese
metabolism, fucoidan--a polyuronic acid of seaweed origin--was found
to reduce the uptake of manganese in tied-off segments of rat
jejunum by up to 77% (51).

The effect of a high-methoxyl pectin (15 g) derived from apples
(Spreda/USA Co., Prospect, KY) was investigated in our laboratory
using the 40 mg manganese tolerance test and the same subjects who
participated in the tests with cellulose. The 15 g doses of
cellulose and pectin were chosen since these are amounts obtainable
from normal diets high in fiber. As shown in Figure 4, the addition
of pectin produced a pronounced depression of the plasma response to
oral manganese ($MnCl_2$). Manganese uptake was significantly ($p<0.05$)
lower at hours 2 and 3 postdose than during the baseline test. In
addition, total area under the response curve for pectin (1.40 ug/L)
was significantly lower than that determined with manganese alone
(3.19 ug/L). Thus the reduction in plasma appearance of manganese
was more pronounced with pectin than when alpha cellulose was
administered to the same subjects. Since pectin may bind bile salts
more effectively than cellulose (42), this could explain the differential effects of pectin and cellulose on manganese uptake.

Phytate. Phytic acid is an organic polyphosphate found widely in
plants, particularly cereals, nuts and legumes. It has been shown
to complex with various divalent cations in the gastrointestinal
tract and thus reduce mineral bioavailability (33,44,52). Davis et
al. (53) reported that feeding a diet based on isolated soybean

protein, which is known to be high in phytate concentration, inter-
fered with utilization of manganese and thus increased the requirement in chicks. Furthermore, Davies and Nightingale (40) found a
marked reduction in whole-body retention of manganese in young rats
fed a diet providing 10 g/kg phytate.

Experiments in this laboratory examined the effects of small
(100 and 300 mg) doses of sodium phytate administered in capsule
form on plasma uptake of 50 mg of $MnCl_2$. As shown in Figure 5, the
300 mg dose of phytate produced a moderate reduction in manganese
response, which was manifested chiefly at hours three and four of
the test. The relatively modest effect of phytate on manganese
uptake is somewhat unexpected, since it has been shown that phytic
acid may be a more potent inhibitor of trace element absorption than
dietary fibers (35). However, the doses of sodium phytate administered to our subjects were much smaller than the typical daily
intake of 600 to 800 mg (54). Thus we are now investigating the
effects of larger doses of phytate on manganese uptake.

Conclusions

In a series of manganese tolerance tests, three dietary components
--cellulose, pectin, and phytate--were found to reduce plasma uptake
of manganese. Although the amount of manganese administered (40-50
mg) in these tolerance tests was much larger than that typically
consumed (0.9 to 7.0 mg per day) (55,56), the results were similar
to those obtained in bioavailability studies with other trace
elements. Thus it appears that diets high in fiber and phytates
also reduce the bioavailability of manganese.

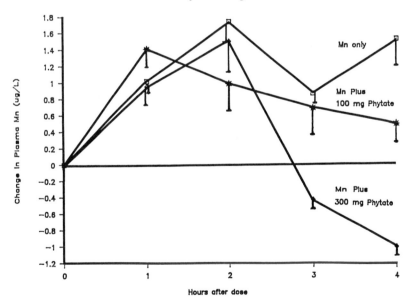

Figure 5: Effect of 100 and 300 mg of sodium phytate on plasma
uptake of 50 mg of manganese (n=3).

Acknowledgments

This work was supported in part by USDA grant #84-CRCR-1-1497 and
NIH Biomedical Research Support Grant RR07-091-21.

Literature Cited

1. Recommended Dietary Allowances, National Academy of Sciences,
    1980, 9th ed.
2. Leach, R.M. Bull. N.Y. Acad. Med. 1984, 60, 172-176.
3. Mena, I.; Horiuchi, K.; Burke, K.; Cotzias, G.C.; Neurology
    1969, 19, 1000-1006.
4. Thomson, A.B.R.; Olatunbosun, D; Valberg, L.S. J. Lab. Clin.
    Med. 1971, 78, 642-655.
5. Garcia-Aranda, J.A.; Wapnir, R.A.; Lifshitz, F. J. Nutr. 1983,
    113, 2601-2607.
6. Gibbons, R.A.; Dixon, S.N.; Hallis, K,; Russell, A.M.; Sansom,
    B.F.; Symonds, H.W. Biochimica et Biophysica Acta 1976, 444,
    1-10.
7. Bertinchamps, A.J.; Miller, S.T.; Cotzias, G.C. Am. J. Physiol.
    1966, 211, 217-224.
8. Britton, A.A.; Cotzias, G.C. Am. J. Physiol. 1966, 211,
    203-206.
9. Papavasiliou, P.S.; Miller, S.T.; Cotzias, G.C. Am J. Physiol.
    1966, 211, 211-216.
10. Lee, D.Y.; Johnson, P.E.; Am. J. Clin. Nutr. 1986, 43, 132
    (abstr.).
11. Abrams, E.; Lassiter, J.W.; Miller, W.J.; Neathery, M.W.;
    Gentry, R.P.; Blackmon, D.M. J. Animal Sci. 1977, 45,
    1108-1113.
12. Carter, J.C.; Miller, W.J.; Neathery, M.W.; Gentry, R.P.;
    Stake, P.E.; Blackmon, D.M. J. Animal Sci. 1974, 42, 1284-2708.
13. Abrams, E.; Lassiter, J.W.; Miller, W.J.; Neathery, M.W.;
    Gentry, R.P.; Scarth, R.D. J. Animal Sci. 1976, 42, 631-636
14. Janghorbani, M.; Young, V.R. Fed. Proc. 1982, 41, 2701-2708.
15. Schilling, J.L.; Muller-Hess, S.; Thonney, F. Lancet, 1973, 2,
    968-969.
16. Fickel, J.J.; Freeland-Graves, J.H.; Robey, M.J. Am. J. Clin.
    Nutr. 1986, 43, 47-58.
17. Solomons, N.W.; Marchini, J.S.; Duarte-Favaro, R.M.; Vannuchi,
    H.; Dutra de Oliveira, J.E. Am. J. Clin. Nutr. 1983, 37,
    566-571.
18. Oelshlegel, F.J.; Brewer, G.J. In Zinc Metabolism: Current
    Aspects in Health and Disease; Alan R. Liss, Inc: New York,
    1977; p. 299-316.
19. Versieck, J.; Cornelis, R. Analytica Chimica Acta, 1980, 116,
    217-254.
20. Cotzias, G.C.; Miller, S.T.; Edwards, J. J. Lab. Clin. Med.
    1966, 67, 836-849.
21. Clydesdale, F.M. Food Tech 1983, Oct., 133-144.
22. King, B.D.; Lassiter, J.W.; Neathery, M.W.; Miller, W.J.;
    Gentry, R.P. J. Animal Sci. 1979, 49, 1235-1241.
23. Watson, L.T.; Ammerman, C.B.; Miller, S.M.; Harms, R.H.
    Poultry Sci. 1971, 50, 1693-1700.

24. Henry, P.R.; Ammerman, C.B., Miles, R.D. Poultry Sci. 1986, 65, 983-986.
25. Black, J.R.; Ammerman, C.B.; Henry, P.R.; Miles, R.D. Poultry Sci. 1984, 63, 1999-2006.
26. Southern, L.L.; Baker, D.H. Poultry Sci. 1983, 62, 642-646.
27. Hennig, A.; Anke, M.; Jeroch, H.; Kaltwasser, W.; Wiedner, W.; Hoffman, G.; Diettrich, M.; Marcy, H. Biol. Abs. 1967, 48, 75618.
28. Cotzias, G.C.; Horiuchi, K.; Fuenzalida, S.; Mena, I. Neurology, 1968, 18, 376-382.
29. Burkitt, D.P.; Walker, A.R.P.; Painter, N.S. J. Am. Med. Assoc. 1974, 229, 1068-1074.
30. Painter, N.S.; Burkitt, D.P. Br. Med. J. 1971, 2, 450-454.
31. Jiang, K.S. J. Nutr. 1986, 116, 999-1006.
32. Gordon, D.T.; Besch-Williford, C.; Ellersieck, M.R. J. Nutr. 1983, 113, 2545-2556.
33. Ismail-Beigi, F.; Reinhold, J.G.; Faradji, B.; Abadi, P. J. Nutr. 1977, 107, 510-518.
34. Sandstead, H.H.; Klevay, L.M.; Jacob, R.A.; Munoz, J.M.; Logan, G.M.; Reck, S.J. In Dietary Fibers: Chemistry and Nutrition; Inglett, G.E. & Falkehag, S.I. Eds.; Academic: New York, 1979; p. 147-156.
35. Erdman, J. Cereal Chem. 1981, 58, 21-26.
36. Reinhold, J.G.; Faradji, B.; Abadi, P.; Ismail-Beigi, F. J. Nutr. 1976, 106, 493-503.
37. Halpin, K.M.; Baker, D.H. Poultry Sci. 1986, 65, 1371-1374.
38. Schwartz, R.; Apgar, B.J.; Wien, E.M. Am. J. Clin. Nutr. 1986, 43, 444-455.
39. Kelsay, J.L. Cereal Chem. 1981, 58, 2-5.
40. Davies, N.T.; Nightingale, R.B. J. Nutr. 1975, 34, 243-258.
41. Story, J.A.; Kritchevsky, D. J. Nutr. 1976, 106, 1291-1294.
42. Mueller, M.A.; Cleary, M.P.; Kritchevsky, D. J. Nutr. 1983, 113, 2229-2238.
43. Godara, R.; Kaur, A.P.; Bhat, C.M. Am. J. Clin. Nutr. 1981, 34, 1083-1086.
44. Slavin, J.L.; Marlett, J.A. Am. J. Clin. Nutr. 1980, 33, 1932-1939.
45. Reinhold, J.G.; Ismail-Beigi, F.; Faradji, B. Nutr. Rep. Int. 1975, 12, 75-85.
46. Ranhotra, G.S.; Lee, C.; Gelroth, J.A. Nutr. Rep. Int. 1979, 19, 851-857.
47. Furda, I. In Dietary Fibers: Chemistry and Nutrition; Inglett, G.E. & Falkehag, S.I. Eds.; Academic: New York, 1979; p. 31-48.
48. Kay, R.M.; Truswell, A.S. Am. J. Clin. Nutr. 1977, 30, 171-175.
49. Sandberg, A.-S.; Ahderinne, R.; Andersson, H.; Hallgren, B.; Hulten, L. Human Nutr. Clin. Nutr. 1983, 37C, 171-183.
50. Monnier, L.; Colette, C.; Aquirre, L.; Mirauze, J. Am. J. Clin. Nutr. 1980, 33, 1225-1232.
51. Becker, G.; Osterloh, K.; Schafer, S.; Forth, W.; Paskins-Hurlburt, A.J.; Tanaka, G.; Skoryna, S.C. Digestion, 1981, 21, 6-12.
52. Sandberg, A.-S.; Hasselblad, C.; Hasselblad, K. Br. J. Nutr. 1982, 48, 185-191.

53. Davis, P.N.; Norris, L.C.; Kratzer, F.H. J. Nutr. 1962, 77, 217–223.
54. Davies, N.T. In Dietary Fiber in Health and Disease; Vahouny, G.V. & Kritchevsky, D. Eds.; Plenum: New York, 1982; p. 105–116.
55. Waslien, C.I. In Trace Elements in Human Health and Disease; Prasad, A.S. & Oberleas, D. Eds.; Academic: New York, 1976; Vol. II, p. 347–370.
56. Patterson, K.Y.; Holbrook, J.T.; Bodner, J.E.; Kelsay, J.L.; Smith, J.C.; Veillon, C. Am. J. Clin. Nutr. 1984, 40, 1397–1403.

RECEIVED December 1, 1986

Chapter 12

Manganese and Lipid Metabolism as Affected by Dietary Manganese and Fat

Jan M. Johnson[1] and Constance Kies

Department of Human Nutrition and Food Service Management,
University of Nebraska, Lincoln, NE 68583

Two studies were conducted to investigate the
effects of dietary manganese and fat on manganese
and lipid metabolism. In Study I, 80 male, weanling
rats were fed two levels of dietary fat (5% and
25%). Serum, liver and brain lipid concentrations,
body weight change and fecal fat excretions were
greater in rats fed the diet with 25% fat. Within
each level of fat, total liver lipids decreased
and liver cholesterol increased as level of dietary
manganese increased. Serum cholesterol levels were
highest when manganese was fed at 50 and 500 mg/kg
diet. Manganese intake, fecal manganese excretion
and whole blood manganese increased as level of
dietary manganese increased. Dietary treatments
had no effect on liver manganese concentrations.
In Study II, young adult human subjects were fed
two laboratory-controlled diets containing either
30% of total calories from fat (approximately 100
mg cholesterol; 10:10:10 PUFA to MUFA to SFA
ratio) or 40% of total calories from fat (approximately 600 mg cholesterol; 4:14:14 fatty acid
ratio). Two levels of manganese were fed (5 and
45 mg Mn/day) within each level of fat. The higher
level of dietary fat generally increased fecal
excretion of manganese and increased serum lipids.
Dietary supplementation with 40 mg of manganese
increased both fecal excretion and whole blood
concentration of the mineral but had no effect
on serum lipids or fecal fat.

At least in part because atherosclerosis and coronary heart
disease continue to be the number one cause of death among North
Americans, interest in interactions between dietary constituents

[1]Current address: Department of Home Economics, Illinois State University,
Normal, IL 61761

remains high. Several reports of an association of manganese with
steroid biosynthesis and lipid metabolism have been published (1).
     Curran and Clute (1) demonstrated an in vitro increase in chol-
esterol synthesis in rat liver cell clusters injected with manganese.
In a similar experiment, Curran (2) injected several transition
elements (V, Ti, Cr, Mn, Fe, Co, Ni, Cu and Zn) intraperitoneally
into rats. After one hour the rats were sacrificed and the livers
from each group were pooled and incubated with sodium acetate-1-C^{14}.
Manganese and chromium were found to increase incorporation of
acetate into cholesterol by 100 percent, whereas vanadium depressed
cholesterol synthesis by 50 percent.
     Manganese acts as a cofactor of mevalonate kinase and farnesyl
pyrophosphate synthetase. Mevalonate kinase and possibly one other
manganese-activated enzyme are necessary for the formation of
mevalonate from acetate (3). Farnesyl pyrophosphate synthetase acts
to add one 5-carbon unit to geranyl pyrophosphate to make farnesyl
pyrophosphate (4) (Figure 1).
     Little is known of the in vivo effect of manganese on choles-
terol metabolism. Doisy (6) observed a decrease in serum cholesterol (from 206 to 80 mg/dl) in a single manganese deficient human
subject. Reports of other human studies conducted to determine the
influence of dietary manganese on cholesterol metabolism were not
found.
     Recently, Klimis-Tavantzis and coworkers (7,8) reported results
of a series of studies designed to investigate the effects of
dietary manganese deficiency on cholesterol and lipid metabolism in
two experimental animal models. Day-old chicks were fed a manganese-
deficient (4.8 μg/g) or a manganese-supplemented (104.8 μg/g) diet
for 4 weeks after which an injection of estrogen was given. Manganese deficiency did not significantly alter plasma cholesterol or
liver cholesterol. When older (36-week-old) laying hens were given
similar diets (7), they demonstrated decreased hepatic manganese
and cholesterol concentrations. These hens also tended to have increased total liver lipid concentrations.
     Weanling, Wistar and RICO (genetically hypercholesterolemic)
rats were placed on manganese-deficient (0.12 μg Mn/g) or manganese-
sufficient (100.12 μg Mn/g) diets. Plasma total, VLDL- and HDL-
cholesterol levels, and liver cholesterol and lipid concentrations
were not affected by the treatment used. These results suggest that
dietary manganese deficiency does not result in significant alterations in cholesterol and lipid metabolism in the rat (8).
     Manganese has a further role as a lipotropic agent. Amdur and
associates (9) found that hepatic lipid concentration was increased
by manganese deficiency. Plumlee et al. (10) conducted four experiments to determine the effect of manganese deficiency in swine and
found that total body fat and liver lipid concentrations were increased by manganese deficiency.
     It has been characteristic of nutrition studies to use one
nutrient alteration experimental design to investigate one possible
effect. However, in order to elucidate dietary relationships with
pathological conditions, it may be necessary to use interaction-type
studies. Therefore, the overall objective of the research conducted
in our laboratories was to investigate the effect of dietary fat-
manganese interactions on cholesterol synthesis.

Experimental Plan - Study I

Two studies were used to investigate the effects of dietary manganese and fat on manganese and lipid metabolism. The purpose of the first study was to determine the interactions among four levels of dietary manganese and two levels of dietary fat on manganese and lipid status of male weanling rats.

Male, weanling, Sprague-Dawley inbred rats (Harlan/Sprague/Dawley, Madison, WI) were used. After three days of adjustment, the 80 rats were randomly assigned to one of eight dietary treatment groups. Two levels of dietary fat (5 percent and 25 percent of the diets by weight) and four levels of dietary manganese (5, 50, 500 and 5000 mg/kg diet) were fed.

The composition of the basal 5 percent and 25 percent fat diets is shown in Table I. All ingredients were purchased from Teklad (Madison, WI) except for the hydrogenated vegetable oil and the corn starch which were purchased in single lots from a local supermarket. Corn starch was used to balance the fat content of the two basal diets. The animals were allowed feed and distilled water ad libitum for 56 days. Treatment variations are shown in Table II.

Table I. Composition of Experimental Rations

Ingredient	Amount/kg	
	5% Fat	25% Fat
Casein	20 g	20 g
DL-methionine	300 mg	300 mg
Crisco shortening	5 g	25 g
Corn starch	45 g	25 g
Sucrose	20 g	20 g
Cellulose	5 g	5 g
AIN mineral mix[1]	3.5 g	3.5 g
AIN vitamin mix	1 g	1 g
Choline bitartrate	200 mg	200 mg

[1]Mineral mix without manganese. Manganese to supply 5, 50, 500 and 5000 mg/kg diet as manganese carbonate (Teklad, Madison, WI) was added at the expense of sucrose to create rations varied in manganese content.

Feed intakes and body weights were recorded on a weekly basis. Feces were collected daily and composited into 7-day lots. At the end of the study, a 12-hour fasting blood sample was collected from each rat. The brain and liver of each animal was excised and frozen. Liver, whole blood and feed manganese was measured using a Varian Techtron Atomic Absorption Spectrophotometer Model 1275. Total liver lipid was extracted from lyphilized tissue and determined by the method described by Folch et al. (11). Serum total cholesterol and HDL-cholesterol were also enzymatically assayed (12). Fecal fat analyses were performed using the Goldfisch method (13).

Table II. Dietary Treatment Variations

Treatment Number	Fat (g/kg)	Manganese[1] (mg/kg)
1	5	5
2	25	5
3	5	50
4	25	50
5	5	500
6	25	500
7	5	5000
8	25	5000

[1]Manganese carbonate (Teklad, Madison, WI).

Results and Discussion - Study I

Mean serum total cholesterol levels are shown in Figure 2. For rats consuming the high fat diets, serum total cholesterol levels were highest when 50 mg Mn/kg diet was fed, although the value was not significantly higher than values attained on other high fat diets. For rats consuming the low fat diets, mean serum cholesterol levels were significantly higher for the 50 and 500 mg Mn/kg diet treatments (P<0.05). Perhaps the lower fat intake allowed the effect of manganese intake on lipid metabolism to become more pronounced.

Figure 3 shows the mean serum HDL-cholesterol levels of rats fed low and high fat dietary treatments as affected by level of dietary manganese. HDL-cholesterol levels were higher for rats fed the high fat diets than for rats fed the low fat diets at each level of dietary manganese except at the 500 mg Mn/kg diet level. When the data were grouped according to dietary manganese alone, serum HDL-cholesterol levels of rats fed the lowest level of manganese were significantly higher than were those of rats consuming the highest level of manganese.

As can be seen in Figure 4, liver lipid concentrations were higher for rats fed high fat diets (within each level of dietary manganese) than for rats fed low fat diets. These differences were significant for each level of dietary manganese fed (P<0.05). Within each level of fat fed, liver total lipid concentrations decreased as level of dietary manganese increased.

Figure 5 illustrates the increase in liver cholesterol concentration which occurs with an increase in dietary manganese. Within each level of manganese fed, liver cholesterol concentrations were higher for rats consuming the high fat diets, although these differences were only significant at the lowest and highest levels of dietary manganese (P<0.05).

Mean liver manganese concentrations are shown in Table III. Means did not differ significantly. Liver manganese concentrations did not seem to reflect the level of dietary manganese consumed.

Whole blood levels of manganese reflected differences in levels of dietary manganese. As shown in Figure 6, whole blood manganese concentrations of rats fed both low fat and high fat diets tended to increase as level of dietary manganese increased.

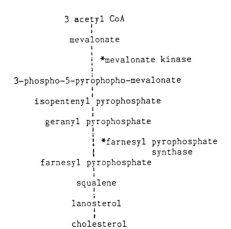

Figure 1. Pathway of cholesterol biosynthesis.

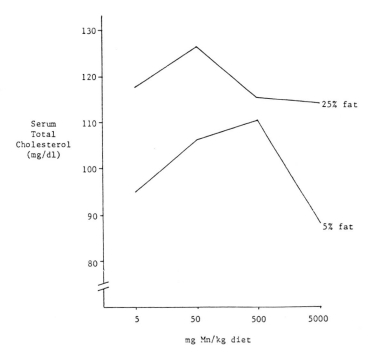

Figure 2.   Serum total cholesterol levels (mg/dl) as affected by dietary manganese and fat.

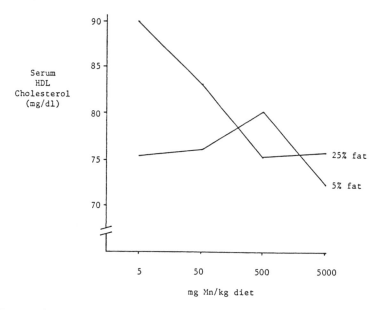

Figure 3. Serum HDL-cholesterol levels (mg/dl) as affected by dietary manganese and fat.

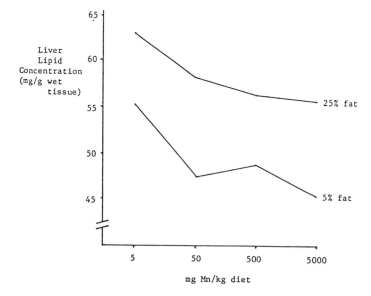

Figure 4. Liver lipid concentrations (mg/g wet tissue) as affected by dietary manganese and fat.

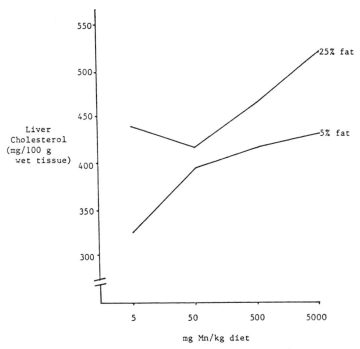

Figure 5.   Liver cholesterol concentrations (mg/100 g wet tissue) as affected by dietary manganese and fat.

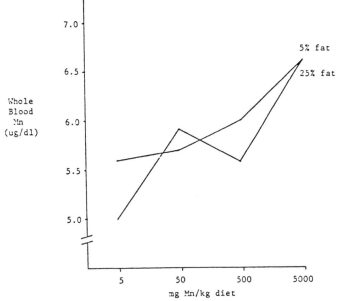

Figure 6.   Whole blood manganese levels (µg/dl) as affected by dietary manganese and fat.

Table III. Mean Liver Manganese Concentrations (µg/g wet tissue)
            in Rats Fed Varying Levels of Manganese and Fat

Dietary Manganese mg/kg	Dietary Fat (%)	
	5	25
5	4.0 ± 1.0	5.0 ± 0.9
50	3.7 ± 1.7	3.5 ± 1.4
500	4.7 ± 2.4	4.0 ± 1.7
5000	4.5 ± 2.7	3.8 ± 2.1

As shown in Figure 7, rats excreted approximately five to six
times more fat when receiving the high fat diets compared to the
low fat diets. Since the high fat diets contained five times as
much fat as did the low fat diets it appeared that fecal fat excretion of the rats was proportional to the fat content of the diets.
This is perhaps due to the relatively poor ability of the rat to
utilize fat. For the high fat treatments, fecal fat excretions of
rats fed the lowest and highest levels of dietary manganese were
significantly different from each other and from excretions of rats
fed the other two levels of dietary manganese ($P<0.05$). With the
lwo fat ration, however, there were no significant differences in
fecal fat excretion attributable to level of dietary manganese.

Body weight changes (g/8 week period) as affected by dietary
manganese and fat are shown in Figure 8. Rats consuming 50 mg Mn/
kg diet gained the most weight on each level of dietary fat, while
those consuming the diets containing the lowest and highest levels
of manganese gained the least. No significant main effects of
dietary manganese occurred. Thus, significant differences in body
weight change may be attributed to differences in dietary fat alone.

Experimental Plan - Study II

The purpose of the second study was to determine the effect of
changes in kind and amount of dietary fat, with or without manganese
supplementation, on blood serum cholesterol and triglyceride levels
and on manganese status of human adults. The project was comprised
of a 5-day pre-period and four, 14-day experimental periods.

During the experimental periods, two constant, laboratory-
controlled diets were fed. The "usual" U.S. diet (U.F.) was
formulated to contain 40 percent of total calories from fat, 600 mg
cholesterol, and polyunsaturated to monounsaturated to saturated
fatty acids in a ratio of 4:14:14. The modified fat diet (M.F.)
contained 30 percent of total calories from fat, approximately 100
mg cholesterol, and a polyunsaturated to monounsaturated to saturated
fatty acid ratio of approximately 10:10:10.

The four experimental periods were divided into parts A and B,
with each part composed of two experimental periods. Within each
part the following variations were used: basal diet alone (either
U.F. or M.F.) or the basal diet plus a 40 mg manganese supplement
(as manganese gluconate amino acid chelate) (Table IV).

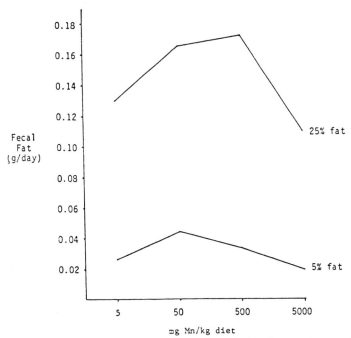

Figure 7.   Mean fecal fat excretion (g/day) as affected by dietary manganese and fat.

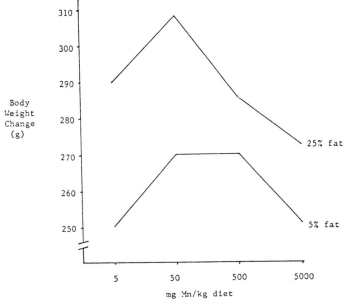

Figure 8.   Body weight change (g/8 week period) as affected by dietary manganese and fat.

Table IV. Experimental Plan for Study II

Period[1]	No. of Days	Diet Type and Modification
Pre-period	5	Self-selected, self-recorded
Part A		
1	14	Controlled, usual U.S. diet
2	14	Controlled, usual U.S. diet + 40 mg Mn/day
Part B		
1	14	Controlled, fat modified diet
2	14	Controlled, fat modified diet + 40 mg Mn/day

[1]Fourteen subjects; order of periods arranged according to a double, cross-over design.

Subjects were 14 healthy men and women who lived in the human metabolic unit of the Department of Human Nutrition and Food Service Management at the University of Nebraska-Lincoln. All meals were prepared and consumed in the metabolic diet kitchen. Subjects made complete urine and fecal collections throughout the study and donated blood samples biweekly.

The manganese content of the basal diets and of urine, feces and whole blood was measured using a Varian Techtron Atomic Absorption Spectrophotometer Model 1275. Urine samples were read directly using a graphite furnace attachment (Model GTA-95). Fecal composites were analyzed for fat content (13). Serum total cholesterol and HDL-cholesterol were enzymatically assayed (12,14). Serum triglycerides were assayed spectrophotometrically based on the method of Fletcher (15).

Results and Discussion - Study II

The mean manganese intakes are shown in Table V. Mean manganese intakes differed significantly among dietary treatments. Whole wheat bread, a good source of manganese, supplied extra calories to those subjects who began losing weight during the experimental portion of the study. Since weight loss was more prevalent during the M.F. periods than when the U.F. diet was fed, the mean manganese intake was higher when the M.F. diet was fed. Manganese intakes during the supplemented periods were at least six times greater than during the non-supplemented periods. Therefore, effects of manganese intakes on manganese and lipid metabolism may be attributed to supplementation versus non-supplementation.

Fecal manganese losses (Table V) were significantly higher during periods of manganese supplementation than during non-supplemented periods. Significantly more manganese was excreted during the U.F. + Mn period than during the M.F. + Mn period suggesting that manganese utilization from this supplement was affected by differences in fat content of the two diets (either total amount or type of dietary fat).

Table V. Mean Manganese Intakes (mg/day) and Fecal Manganese
Excretions (mg/day) of Humans Fed Varying Levels of Manganese
and Fat

	Diet[1]				
	Pre-	MF	MF+Mn	UF	UF+Mn
Manganese intake (mg/day)	5.68[d] ±2.70	7.18[c] ±0.85	47.20[a] ±0.80	5.85[d] ±0.88	45.61[b] ±0.54
Fecal manganese (mg/day)	3.68[c] ±1.55	5.55[c] ±2.43	32.29[b] ±12.14	5.73[c] ±2.84	46.89[a] ±11.69

[1]Diet Code: Pre- = Self-selected diet
             UF = Usual U.S. diet
             MF = Modified fat diet
             Mn = Manganese supplement (40 mg/day)

As shown in Table VI, urinary excretion of manganese did not
differ significantly among the four dietary treatment periods. No
explanation can be offered for the high urinary manganese losses
that occurred during the pre-period.

Mean manganese balances are also shown in Table VI. Manganese
balances were significantly higher during the MF+Mn period than
during any other period. This agrees with the data on fecal manganese excretion and indicates that supplemental manganese may be
absorbed and retained by the body more efficiently during consumption of a low fat diet than during consumption of a high fat diet.

Table VI. Mean Urinary Manganese Excretion (μg/day),
Manganese Balance (mg/day) and Whole Blood Manganese (μg/dl) in
Humans Fed Varying Levels of Manganese and Fat

	Diet[1]				
	Pre-	MF	MF+Mn	UF	UF+Mn
Urinary manganese (μg/day)	9.86[a] ±4.11	6.99[b] ±3.04	7.80[ab] ±3.07	7.93[ab] ±3.19	7.70[ab] ±2.40
Manganese balance (mg/day)	1.70[b] ±3.21	1.63[b] ±2.45	14.91[a] ±12.47	0.11[b] ±2.77	-1.37[b] ±11.72
Whole blood manganese (μg/dl)	2.43[c] ±0.36	2.70[b] ±0.28	2.90[a] ±0.15	2.55[bc] ±0.29	2.91[a] ±0.17

[1]Diet Code: Pre- = Self-selected diet
             UF = Usual U.S. diet
             MF = Modified fat diet
             Mn = Manganese supplement (40 mg/day)

Mean whole blood manganese levels (Table VI) were significantly
higher during periods of manganese supplementation. This would not
have been expected during the UF+Mn period since manganese balance
for this period was -1.37 mg/day. This would suggest that the high
fecal manganese excretion during this period was actually due to an

increase in endogenous secretion of manganese into the gastrointestinal tract rather than to a decreased absorption of the mineral.

Serum lipid values are shown in Table VII. There were no significant effects of either dietary fat or manganese on serum cholesterol levels during the experimental periods. However, total
cholesterol levels tended to be lower when the MF diet was fed than
when the UF diet was used (P<0.10).

Serum HDL-cholesterol values were significantly higher for the
UF diet treatments than for the MF diet treatments (P<0.05). There
were no differences, however, in manganese-supplemented versus non-
supplemented periods within the same level of dietary fat.

While mean triglyceride levels were higher for the UF and UF+Mn
periods than for the lower fat periods, the difference was only
significant for the manganese-supplemented (MF+Mn versus UF+Mn,
P<0.005) period. No effect of dietary manganese on serum triglyceride levels was seen.

Table VII. Mean Serum Cholesterol, HDL-Cholesterol and
Triglyceride Levels (mg/dl) in Humans Fed Varying Levels of
Manganese and Fat

| | Diet[1] | | | |
	Pre-	MF	MF+Mn	UF	UF+Mn
Serum total cholesterol (mg/dl)	207.4^a ±34.2	169.1^b ±30.8	177.0^b ±30.8	192.8^{ab} ±33.7	191.1^{ab} ±48.7
Serum HDL- cholesterol (mg/dl)	46.7^b ±9.0	47.6^b ±5.74	48.0^b ±6.46	63.6^a ±6.58	62.6^a ±9.65
Serum triglycerides (mg/dl)	55.6^c ±14.6	80.2^{ab} ±11.5	73.3^b ±8.1	88.1^a ±13.9	88.3^a ±11.5

[1]Diet Code: Pre- = Self-selected diet
              UF = Usual U.S. diet
              MF = Modified fat diet
              Mn = Manganese supplement (40 mg/day)

No significant differences were found in mean fecal fat excretions (Table VIII). Failure to detect differences in fecal fat may
indicate that the increase in total fat content of the usual versus
the modified fat diet is compensated for by an increase in absorption of fat. Increased absorption of fat, then, could account for
the higher serum HDL-cholesterol and triglycerides levels caused by
the two higher fat treatments.

In conclusion, serum, liver and brain lipid concentrations,
body weight change and fecal fat excretions were greater in rats fed
a diet with 25% fat than in rats fed a lower fat diet. Within each
level of fat, total liver lipids decreased and liver cholesterol
concentration increased as level of dietary manganese increased.
However, in 14 adult, human subjects fed two levels of dietary fat,
dietary manganese had no effect on serum lipid parameters or fecal
fat excretion.

Table VIII. Mean Fecal Fat Excretions (g/day) of Humans Fed Varying Levels of Manganese and Fat

	Diet[1]				
	Pre-	MF	MF+Mn	UF	UF+Mn
Fecal fat (g/day)	2.39^a	2.21^a	2.36^a	1.57^a	2.21^a
	±1.40	±1.10	±1.33	±0.68	±1.09

[1]Diet Code: Pre- = Self-selected diet
UF = Usual U.S. diet
MF = Modified fat diet
Mn = Manganese supplement (40 mg/day)

Acknowledgments

Published as Paper Number 8243, Journal Series, Agricultural Research Division, University of Nebraska, Lincoln, Nebraska 68583. Supported by U.S.D.A., C.S.R.S. Regional Research Projects NC-167 and W-143 and University of Nebraska Agricultural Research Division Project 91-031.

Literature Cited

1. Curran, G.L.; Clute, O.L. J. Biol. Chem. 1953, 204, 215-219.
2. Curran, G. J. Biol. Chem. 1954, 210, 765-770.
3. Amdur, B.; Rilling, H.; Bloch, K. J. Chem. Soc. 1957, 79, 2646-2647.
4. Benedict, C.; Kett, J.; Porter, J. Arch. Biochem. Biophys. 1965, 110, 611-621.
5. Bloch, K.S. Science 1965, 150, 19-28.
6. Doisy, E.A., Jr. In Trace Element Metabolism in Animals; Hoekstra, W.G.; Suttie, J.W.; Ganther, H.E.; Mertz, W., Ed.; University Park Press: Baltimore, 1974; p. 668-670.
7. Klimis-Tavantzis, D.J.; Kris-Etherton, P.M.; Leach, R.M., Jr. J. Nutr. 1983, 113, 320-327.
8. Klimis-Tavantzis, D.J.; Leach, R.M., Jr.; Kris-Etherton, R.M. J. Nutr. 1983, 113, 328-336.
9. Amdur, M.O.; Norris, L.C.; Heuser, G.F. J. Biol. Chem. 1946, 164, 783-784.
10. Plumbee, M.P.; Thrasher, D.M.; Beeson, W.M.; Andrews, F.N.; Parker, H.E. J. Ani. Sci. 1956, 15, 352-367.
11. Folch, J.; Lees, M.; Stanley, G.H. J. Biol. Chem. 1957, 226, 497-507.
12. Allain, C.A.; Poon, L.S.; Chan, C.S.G.; Richmond, W.; Fu, P.C. Clin. Chem. 1974, 20, 470-475.
13. _____ . In AOAC Official Method of Analysis; Williams, S., Ed.; Byrd Press: Richmond, 1984; 14th ed., p. 159.
14. Lopes-Virella, M.F.; Stone, P.; Eliss, S.; Colwell, J.A. Clin. Chem. 1977, 23, 882-884.
15. Fletcher, M.J. Clin. Chem. Acta. 1968, 22, 393-397.

RECEIVED July 17, 1987

Chapter 13

Manganese Availability for Humans
Effect of Selected Dietary Factors

Constance Kies, K. D. Aldrich, Jan M. Johnson, C. Creps, C. Kowalski, and R. H. Wang

Department of Human Nutrition and Food Service Management, University of Nebraska, Lincoln, NE 68583

The objective of the project was to determine the effect of several dietary constituents on manganese bioavailability of young adult humans. In a series of studies, human subjects were fed constant, laboratory-controlled diets in order to create a background against which several different dietary variations could be tested during treatment periods ranging from seven to 28 days. Manganese contents of food, feces, urine and whole blood were analyzed using a carbon rod attachment on an atomic absorption spectrophotometer. At low manganese intake levels, manganese bioavailability was apparently enhanced by ascorbic acid and by meat-containing diets but was possibly inhibited by iron, ascorbic acid (at high manganese intake levels) and by some dietary fiber sources.

Recommended and/or projected changes in the American diet indirectly may change intakes of specific nutrients or of availability of specific nutrients in unpredicted or unpredictable ways. Dietary fiber, ascorbic acid and dietary fat have all been shown to affect the availability of some nutrient minerals. Hence, it is not unreasonable to assume that alterations in intake of these dietary constituents might have a direct effect on the bioavailability of manganese or might indirectly affect manganese bioavailability by, for example, affecting the availability of other minerals with which manganese competes for absorption sites. Stress on reduced caloric intake to avoid obesity has received a particularly attentive audience among American women. Ideally, dietary reduction in calories is achieved via decreased consumption of empty-calorie foods which leaves consumption of vitamins and minerals unchanged. In "real world" situations, a decrease in caloric consumption almost invariably leads to a decreased intake of all nutrients.

Impact of dietary factors on manganese bioavailability and on manganese nutritional status have not been extensively investigated. The objective of the current project was to determine effects of alterations in iron, ascorbic acid, fiber and meat intake on manganese utilization by young human adults.

Procedures (General)

In a series of studies ranging from 14 to 56 days each, adult human subjects were fed constant, measured, laboratory controlled diets. Diets were based on ordinary foods and included the following items: milk, unenriched 70% flour bread (plus wheat bran in some studies), ready-to-eat oat or corn based breakfast cereals, green beans, tomato and orange juice (or apple juice in some studies), peanut butter, ground beef and tuna (or soy isolate products), peaches, pears, potatoes and rice. Water was allowed ad libitum. Jelly, butter and soft drinks were used to adjust caloric intake for each subject to that needed for weight maintenance. Thus, some differences in the basal diets occurred among subjects but diets were maintained constant for any one subject. Experimental variables were superimposed on these basal diets as demanded by the objective of each study as described in greater detail with the results. All food was prepared and eaten under supervision of personnel in the human nutrition metabolic unit special diet kitchen, Department of Human Nutrition and Food Service Management, University of Nebraska.

Each study was divided into experimental periods of 7 to 28 days each. Within each study, all subjects received all experimental variables according to a randomized, cross-over design.

Subjects were all students or employees of the University of Nebraska who maintained their usual work, study and social activities except for the eating of the experimental diets and nothing else, making collections of excreta, giving blood samples, and filling out various questionnaires. All were assumed to be in good health as evaluated from health histories by medical personnel of the University of Nebraska Health Center. Signing of subject consent forms was required of all participants prior to participation. This project was approved for human subject participation by the University of Nebraska Institutional Review Board for the Protection of Human Research Subjects.

Subjects made complete collections of urine and stools throughout each study. Feces for each subject were divided into period lots representing food eaten during each period by use of fecal dyes (brilliant blue and carmine red) and colored glass beads, composited, mixed and sampled for later analyses. Urine for each subject for each day was composited on the basis of time, diluted to a constant volume with distilled water, mixed, sampled and frozen for later analyses. Fasting blood samples were drawn at the beginning of each study and at the end of each experimental period.

Food, urine, feces and whole blood were analyzed for manganese contents using a Varian Model 1150 or 1275 Atomic Absorption Spectrophotometer with carbon rod attachment according to manual directions. Although manganese contents of urine were measured, results are not reported in this paper because of the minute, unchangeable amounts which were found. Whole blood manganese values also will not be reported since this analysis was not performed on samples from all subjects for all studies. Those results which were obtained indicated that whole blood manganese levels were resistant to change in the short term studies which comprised this project.

In evaluation of data obtained, it was assumed that an increase in fecal manganese loss at similar levels of manganese intake denoted a decrease in manganese absorption and utilization. Manganese in the feces may represent exogenous, unabsorbed food manganese or may be endogenous manganese which has been secreted into the gastrointestinal tract. Since this endogenous manganese can be recycled, an increase in fecal manganese loss due to an increase in endogenous fecal manganese loss may even-so be due to dietary constituents.

Apparent manganese retention was calculated by subtracting the fecal manganese loss from the dietary intake. The percent manganese retention was calculated by dividing the manganese retention by the manganese intake and multiplying the resulting figure by 100. An increase in apparent manganese retention or percent manganese retention was assumed to indicate an increase in manganese bioavailability. This would be considered good in situations involving low manganese intakes but the reverse would be true if manganese toxicities are the issue.

Data for each study were subjected to statistical analyses. These tests included analysis of variance and, if the design of the study warranted, Duncan's Multiple Range Test and/or orthogonal contrast.

Manganese Utilization from Omnivore and Vegetarian Diets

Americans are being encouraged to increase their intake of plant-based foods while decreasing their intakes of animal origin products. Since meat, milk, poultry and fish are known to contain only small amounts of manganese, this recommendation would be expected to have little effect on the manganese intake levels of humans. Plant products such as soy which are often used in place of meat in vegetarian diets may contain higher amounts of manganese than does meat but concurrently these foods contain greater amounts of phytates which may inhibit manganese utilization.

The effect of substituting 100 g/subject/day of soy isolate-based products for the 50 g of ground beef and 50 g of tuna/subject/day in the usual basal diet on manganese utilization was investigated in one 56-day study at the University of Nebraska. The project involved two 28-day periods arranged according to a randomized cross-over design for each subject. The subjects were 10 adult women who lived and ate all meals in the departmental metabolic unit. During one period the subjects received the meat diet while, during the other period, the meat-free (soy-containing) diet was given.

As shown in Table I, substitution of 50 g of ground beef and 50 g of tuna fish/subject/day with 100 g/subject/day of soy isolate based products resulted in a significant decrease in apparent manganese retention of the subjects (p<0.05). Because of the slightly higher manganese content of the beef and tuna fish than of the soy isolate replacement products, the meat-containing diet provided slightly more manganese than did the meat-free diet. Even so, fecal manganese losses were greater than when the meat-free diet was fed than when the meat-containing diets were used. This suggests that the manganese in meat is very available and, that meat enhances the bioavailability of manganese from the whole diet.

Because of the change in level of dietary protein, it is not possible to positively determine whether quality of protein or level of protein was the causative factor in change in manganese retention. However, influence of level of dietary protein on manganese bio-availability has been investigated in several other studies with no significant effect being demonstrated (1-3). Numerically, however, manganese balances of human subjects in the Greger and Snedeker study (1) were more positive when receiving the high protein diet than when receiving the low protein diet. Variation in protein intake between the high and low protein diets was considerably greater in that study than was true in the current study. In two other studies conducted at the University of Nebraska, source of dietary protein was demonstrated to influence manganese nutritional status in human subjects (4-6). Thus, it is probable that protein quality rather than protein quantity was the factor influencing manganese utilization. Although not measured, soy isolate products also may contain phytates which may have had an adverse effect on manganese utilization (7).

Table I. Manganese (Mn) Utilization from Meat Containing and Meat-Free Diets

| Parameter | Value when receiving:[1,2] | |
	+ meat diet	− meat diet
Number of subjects	10	10
Mn intake, mg/day	4.94[a]	4.53[a]
Mn fecal loss, mg/day	4.66[a]±0.22	4.71[a]±0.35
Apparent Mn retention, mg/day	+0.28[a]±0.90	−0.18[b]±0.07

[1]Values with different letter superscripts are significantly different from one another ($p < 0.05$).

[2]Based on recalculated data supplied by Aldrich (5).

Wheat Bran as a Source of Manganese for Humans

Wheat bran and whole wheat cereals quantitatively contain high amounts of manganese and are often listed as particularly valuable sources of manganese. However, zinc also is contained in appreciable amounts in wheat bran and whole wheat products but is poorly absorbed by the human from these sources. This has been attributed to either the phytate or the fiber contents of these products or a combination of these two dietary factors. These same factors may also affect the absorption of manganese.

In a series of four studies of 24 days each, the effects of feeding two certified wheat brans on manganese utilization of human adults was investigated. The two wheat brans were obtained from The American Association of Cereal Chemists. This organization has obtained and stockpiled these brans for investigational purposes so as to reduce variations in findings among laboratory investigations of wheat bran as a source of fiber. Each 24-day study was divided into three experimental periods of seven days each during which the basal diet alone, the basal diet plus hard red spring wheat bran (21 g/subject/day) or the basal diet plus soft white spring wheat bran (21 g/subject/day) was fed. Periods were randomly arranged. Brans were incorporated into an unenriched, 70% extracted wheat flour bread. A total of 38 subjects participated in these studies.

As shown in Table II, although wheat brans in this study contained considerable amounts of manganese, apparently little or none of this was available to the human subjects. With the feeding of hard red or soft white wheat bran supplemented bread, fecal losses of manganese were significantly increased (p<0.05). Apparent manganese retention was not significantly different when the red bran bread was fed than when the no bran bread was used; however, significantly less manganese was retained by the subjects when the white bran bread was fed than when either of the other test breads were used. This suggests the possibility that not only was the manganese from the white bran unavailable but that manganese availability from the rest of the diet was adversely affected.

Experimental periods in this study were only seven days in length; hence, with time it is possible that some adaptation might have occurred. In an earlier project, Johnson et al. (8) fed similar diets with the same hard red and soft white wheat bran supplements to adult human subjects for 28 days. Losses of manganese in feces were determined for each of the four 7-day periods comprising the study. Recently, Schwartz et al. (9) reported that over a 48-day feeding period apparent manganese absorption significantly improved with time. However, from the data presented for weeks 2-4 as compared to weeks 5-7, fecal losses of manganese were virtually unchanged but the apparent increase in absorption was a function of the increase in manganese intake (mean 1.1 mg/subject/day) in weeks 5-7 as compared to weeks 2-4.

Table II. Effect of Wheat Bran on Manganese (Mn) Utilization
in Humans

Parameter	Basal Diet		
	Alone	+Red Bran[1]	+White Bran[1]
Number of subjects	59	59	59
Mn intake, mg/day	5.34[c]	8.46[a]	7.90[b]
Fecal Mn, mg/day	4.17[c]±0.32	7.12[a]±0.69	6.46[b]±0.05
Apparent Mn retention, mg/day	1.17[a]±0.18	1.34[a]±0.21	0.44[b]±0.27
Apparent Mn retention, %	21.9[a]	15.8[b]	6.4[c]

[1] 21 g/subject/day, AACC certified red and white wheat brans.

[2] Values with different letter superscripts are significantly different from one another (p<0.05).

[3] Based on recalculated data supplied by Aldrich (5) and Johnson (26).

Effect of Hemicellulose (Psyllium Fiber) on Manganese Utilization

Wheat bran contains several different forms of dietary fiber including hemicellulose. Some but not all purified dietary fiber sources have been found to have an adverse effect on manganese bioavailability (10).

In a series of 28-day studies, the effects of hemicellulose on manganese utilization were investigated. As in the previous studies on wheat bran, the hemicellulose (20 g/subject/day) was incorporated into a bread product. During the two experimental periods, subjects received either the hemicellulose enriched bread or the bread without hemicellulose. Purified psyllium fiber was used as a source of mixed

hemicellulose. Because of its long history of use as a bulk laxative
and because of its frequent use as a fiber source in purified or
semi-purified diets in research studies involving human subjects,
the use of psyllium fiber as a source of hemicellulose is particularly interesting to research scientists in human nutrition. A total
of 60 subjects participated in the studies.

As shown on Table III, the subjects fed 20 g of hemicellulose
from purified psyllium fiber excreted significantly more manganese
in the feces than when they were fed bread without the hemicellulose
supplement. Unlike wheat bran, purified psyllium fiber (sold
commercially as a bulk laxative) contains no manganese or phytates;
hence, any change in fecal manganese excretion when psyllium fiber is
added to human diets can probably be credited to the mixture of
hemicellulose comprising this product.

Table III. Manganese Utilization as Affected by Psyllium
Hemicellulose

Parameter	Basal Diet[1,2]	
	Alone	+ Hemicellulose
Number of subjects	30	30
Mn intake, mg/day	5.34[a]	5.43[a]
Fecal Mn, mg/day	3.01[b]±0.56	3.98[a]±0.62
Apparent Mn retention, mg/day	2.33[a]±0.41	1.45[b]±0.53
Apparent Mn retention, %	43.63[a]	26.70[b]

[1] 20 g/day as psyllium

[2] Values with different letter superscripts are significantly
different from one another ($p<0.05$).

Manganese Utilization from Spinach

Spinach is also an excellent source of manganese. However, spinach
contains high amounts of soluble fiber and oxalic acid. Both of
these factors have been found to inhibit the utilization of iron.
Using two 5-day periods in a cross-over design, manganese utilization from spinach was determined. Subjects (12) consumed their
normal, self-selected, self-recorded diets. During one of the two
randomly arranged periods, subjects were asked to eat one 8 oz. can
of spinach.

The spinach provided an additional 1.10 mg manganese/subject/
day. However, fecal losses of manganese were increased by an almost
identical amount and no significant effect on the apparent negative
manganese balances exhibited by these subjects was found (Table IV).
Thus, although spinach contains high amounts of manganese, its
classification as a good source of manganese must be questioned since
this is evidently not manganese which can be absorbed.

Tea as a Source of Manganese

Tea is a plant origin food containing surprisingly high amounts of
manganese. However, tea also contains high amounts of the poly-
phenolic substance tannin which has been found to have a profoundly
adverse effect on the utilization of such diverse nutrients as pro-

Table IV. Manganese Utilization as Affected by Spinach Consumption

Diet	Mn intake	Mn excretion		Mn Balance
	mg/day	Urine mg/day	Feces mg/day	mg/day
Self-selected	0.89^b	0.031^a	1.21^b	-0.35^a
Self-selected + spinach	1.76^a	0.029^a	1.96^a	-0.23^a

Values with different letter superscripts in each column are
significantly different from one another ($p<0.05$).

tein, thiamin and iron. Using data from laboratory controlled
studies employing use of constant diets, responses of 10 tea drinking
subjects (4 g of dry instant tea per day) were compared to 10 non-tea
or non-coffee drinking, age, sex matched controls from the same
studies.

Tea drinking resulted in an increase in fecal manganese excretion approximately equal to that added to the diets in the form of
tea. Hence, no significant improvement in manganese retention
occurred as the result of tea drinking. This suggests that either
the polyphenols or other constituents of tea rendered the manganese
in tea essentially unusable to the human (Table V).

Table V. Manganese Utilization as Affected by Tea Consumption[1]

Diet	Mn intake	Mn excretion		Mn Balance
	mg/day	Urine mg/day	Feces mg/day	mg/day
Basal	2.15^b	0.014^a	2.20^b	-0.06^a
Basal + tea	3.41^a	0.011^a	3.66^a	-0.26^a

[1] 10 age, sex, weight matched subjects

Values with different letter superscripts in each column are
significantly different from one another ($p<0.05$).

Ascorbic Acid Supplement Use and Manganese Utilization

Manganese exists in several different valence states but is thought
to be absorbed in the reduced state (+2) as is iron. Hence, addition
of ascorbic acid might be expected to enhance the apparent absorption
of manganese.

In a series of five studies of 14 days each, the effects of
ascorbic acid on manganese utilization were investigated. The usual
basal diet was modified to lower the ascorbic acid content by substituting apple juice for the usually-fed orange and tomato juices.

During the two randomly arranged experimental periods of seven days each, the subjects received the experimental diets alone or with a 200 mg/subject/day amino acid supplement. A total of 57 subjects participated in the studies in which the only manganese supplied was by the basal diet (4.91-4.95 mg/subject/day).

Ascorbic acid supplementation of diets significantly enhanced the apparent retention of manganese ($p<0.05$) at low levels of manganese intake. When ascorbic acid was added to the diets, fecal manganese losses were significantly increased in comparison to values when the diet was fed alone ($p<0.05$) as shown on Table VI. At least at two levels of manganese intake, ascorbic acid apparently enhances manganese utilization.

Table VI. Effect of Ascorbic Acid on Manganese Utilization in Humans

	Ascorbic acid intake[1,2]	
Parameter	37 mg/day	237 mg/day
Number of subjects	57	57
Mn intake, mg/day	4.91[a]	4.95[b]
Fecal Mn, mg/day	4.19[a]±0.15	3.95[b]±0.05
Apparent Mn retention, mg/day	+0.72[b]±0.05	+1.00[a]±0.05
Apparent Mn retention, %	14.66[b]	20.20[a]

[1]Values with different letter superscripts are significantly different from one another ($p<0.05$).

[2]Based on recalculated data supplied by Kowalski (17) and Wang (16).

Iron Supplement Use and Manganese Utilization

Ascorbic acid is known to enhance the bioavailability of iron by reducing iron from the +3 to the +2 valence state, the absorbable valence state (11-14). In one study, the effect of ferrous fumarate supplementation on manganese utilization from high and low manganese containing diets was investigated. The 28-day study was divided into four, 7-day, randomly-arranged periods. During these periods the seven subjects received the basal diet alone, the basal diet plus ferrous fumarate (to supply 20 mg iron/subject/day), the basal diet plus manganese gluconate (to supply 40 mg manganese/subject/day) or the basal diet plus a combination of the ferrous fumarate and manganese gluconate supplements. Supplements were given in tablet form at the breakfast meal.

Studies, including the present one, designed to investigate effects of increasing dietary levels of iron on manganese utilization have generally indicated ad adverse effect of dietary iron on manganese absorption from the intestinal tract (15-22). As shown in Table VII, ferrous fumarate supplementation of either low-level or high-level manganese diets resulted in increased fecal manganese losses and decreased manganese retention in comparison to values when the appropriate controlled diets were fed ($p<0.05$).

Table VII.   Manganese Utilization as Affected by Iron Intake
at Two Levels of Manganese Intake

Parameter	Basal Diet[1,2]			
	Alone	+ Mn[3]	+ Fe[4]	+ Fe + Mn
Mn intake, mg/day	4.54[b]	44.56[a]	4.56[b]	44.56[a]
Fecal Mn, mg/day	4.78[d]	37.20[b]	7.22[c]	41.44[a]
	±0.77	±3.10	±0.93	±2.54
Apparent Mn retention, mg/day	-0.24[d]	+7.36[a]	-2.58[c]	+3.12[b]
	±0.09	±0.97	±0.88	±0.08

[1] Values with different letter superscripts were significantly
different from one another ($p < 0.05$).

[2] Based on recalculated data by Creps (15).

[3] 40 mg/day as manganese gluconate amino acid chelate.

[4] 20 mg/day as ferrous fumarate.

Conclusion

Other dietary variables besides those discussed in the present paper
may also affect manganese bioavailability and retention by influencing either absorption or excretory mechanisms. For example,
increased intake of dietary calcium has been found to inhibit apparent absorption of manganese (3,17). Results of studies designed to
investigate effect of dietary phosphorus on manganese bioavailability
have given mixed results (23-25). In other studies conducted at the
University of Nebraska, apparent manganese absorption from various
plant sources by humans was found to be very poor in comparison to
that exhibited by manganese salt supplements or manganese supplied
by a mixed food diet (5,26).

     On the basis of data presented in this paper, apparently some
of the best sources of manganese in terms of amount of manganese
contained per reasonable serving portion are, in fact, poor sources
on the basis of utilizable manganese. Therefore, it may be that
manganese content of food should be expressed in units of utilizable
manganese rather than in gravimetric units per se.

Acknowledgments

Published as University of Nebraska Agricultural Research Division
Journal Article Series No. 8062. Supported by Nebraska Agricultural
Research Division Project 91-031 and USDA, CSRS Project W-143.

Literature Cited

1.   Greger, J.L. and Snedeker, S.N.   J. Nutr. 1980, 110, 2243.
2.   Price, N.O.; Bunce, G.E. and Engel, R.W.   Am. J. Clin. Nutr.
     1970, 23, 258.
3.   Price, N.O. and Bunce, G.E.   Nutr. Reports Int. 1972, 5, 275.
4.   Rojhani, A.   1984.   M.S. Thesis, University of Nebraska-Lincoln.
5.   Aldrich, K.D.   1984.   M.S. Thesis, University of Nebraska-
     Lincoln.
6.   Koszewski, W.M.   1984.   M.S. Thesis, University of Nebraska-
     Lincoln.

7. Davis, N.T. and Nightingale, R. Br. J. Nutr. 1975, 34, 243.
8. Johnson, J.; Kies, C. and Fox, H. XIII International Congress of Nutrition, 1985 (Abstract).
9. Schwartz, R.; Apgar, J. and Wien, E.M. Am. J. Clin. Nutr. 1986, 43, 444.
10. Corrington, J. 1982. M.S. Thesis, University of Nebraska-Lincoln.
11. Kies, C. In Nutritional Bioavailability of Iron; Kies, C., Ed.; American Chemical Society: Washington, DC, 1982, p. 183.
12. Bowering, J.; Sanchez, A.M. and Irwin, M.I. J. Nutr. 1976, 106, 985.
13. Hallberg, L. In Nutrition Review's Present Knowledge in Nutrition, 5th Ed. Nutrition Foundation, Inc.: Washington, DC, 1984, p. 459.
14. Cook, J.D.; March, I.A.; and Lynch, S. Am. J. Clin. Nutr. 1977, 30, 235.
15. Creps, C. 1984. M.S. Thesis, University of Nebraska-Lincoln.
16. Wang, R.H. 1984. M.S. Thesis, University of Nebraska-Lincoln.
17. Kowalski, C. 1983. M.S. Thesis, University of Nebraska-Lincoln.
18. Gruden, N. Reprod. Nutr. Develop. 1980, 20(SA), 1539.
19. Gruden, N. Nutr. Reports Int. 1984, 30, 553.
20. Gruden, N. Nutr. Reports Int. 1977, 15, 577.
21. Gruden, N. and Buben, M. Nutr. Reports Int. 1981, 24, 943.
22. Gruden, N. and Buben, M. Nutr. Reports Int. 1981, 25, 849.
23. Spencer, H.; Asmussen, C.R.; Holtzman, R.B. and Kramer, L. Am. J. Clin. Nutr. 1979, 32, 1867.
24. Schaible, P.J. and Bandemer, S.L. Poult. Sci. 1942, 21, 8.
25. Pound, W.G.; Walter, E.F., Jr.; and Kirtland, D. J. Ani. Sci. 1978, 46, 686.
26. Johnson, J. 1983. M.S. Thesis, University of Nebraska-Lincoln.

RECEIVED May 15, 1987

Chapter 14

Manganese Usage in Humans as Affected by Use of Calcium Supplements

Susan D. McDermott and Constance Kies

Department of Human Nutrition and Food Service Management, University of Nebraska, Lincoln, NE 68583

Calcium has long been implicated as a dietary factor which inhibits the absorption of manganese. Since manganese is better absorbed in the oxidized (+2) than in the reduced state (+3 or +4), any factor which increases gastrointestinal tract pH (increases alkalinity) would be expected to inhibit manganese utilization. Calcium carbonate, a commonly used antacid by humans as well as a calcium nutrient supplement, has been found to have a greater adverse effect on apparent manganese absorption in humans than does milk.

Manganese can exist in several different oxidation states including I, II, III, IV, VI and VII although the most stable salts are those in the oxidation states II, IV, VI and VII (1). Although research on manganese needs of humans is very limited, manganese as a nutrient requirement of plants and factors affecting manganese utilization of soil manganese by plans has received extensive investigation (1). Total manganese is generally accepted as being a poor predictor of manganese extractability (or availability) from soil to the plant. One of the most important agronomic characteristics affecting manganese extractability is that of soil pH. As pH of soils rise (as may occur with addition of lime-calcium oxide to soils),oxidation of manganese II to manganese III and IV is favored which reduces the solubility of manganese and, consequently, its availability to plants. Conversely, manganese toxicity in plants is usually found in acid soils with pH lower than 5.5.

Manganese in the human is also thought to be absorbed maximally in the duodenum in the II valence state. Therefore, as with manganese uptake by plants, the pH of the upper gastro-intestinal tract might be expected to be of importance in the absorption of manganese by the human.

Calcium carbonate preparations for many years have been used by humans in large amounts on a self-prescription basis or as recommended by physicians in control or treatment of upper gastro-intestinal distress conditions which are thought to be related to gastric acid production. These include dyspepsia, peptic ulcers,

0097–6156/87/0354–0146$06.00/0
© 1987 American Chemical Society

gastritis, esophagatitus and hiatal hernia. Antacid calcium carbonate products are available in several forms including tablets, gelatin capsules, chewable wafers, gum, and caramels; hence, calcium release from these products designed to increase pH (lower acidity) in the gastro-intestinal tract would be expected to vary with time.

Recent concern relative to the high incidence of osteoporosis in elderly, female, Americans has resulted in increased usage of calcium supplements. Calcium carbonate contains more calcium per weight unit of the salt than does calcium phosphate, calcium lactate or calcium gluconate; hence, either calcium carbonate or one of the calcium carbonate forms such as oyster shells or dolomite is most often the calcium salt choice for use in a supplement since fewer capsules need to be taken (2). Since calcium carbonate preparations marketed as antacids are often sold at a price lower than are those calcium carbonate preparations marketed as calcium supplements, calcium antacid preparations are currently being used as calcium supplements.

Calcium has long been suspected as adversely affecting the bioavailability of manganese. Excessive intakes of calcium or phosphorus have been shown to increase the daily requirements for manganese in swine (3-5) probably due to decreased absorption of this mineral. However, comparatively little information is available on the comparative effects of different sources of calcium on manganese utilization in humans.

Effects of calcium phosphate and calcium lactate with and without ascorbic acid supplementation were examined in studies reported by Kowalski (6). Calcium phosphate was found to have a greater negative effect on apparent manganese absorption in adult humans as judged on percentage of dietary manganese recovered in feces in comparison to values when calcium lactate or no calcium supplements were given (Table I). Ascorbic acid supplements tended to negate the negative effects of calcium supplementation.

Table I. Calcium (Ca) Supplementation and Manganese (Mn) Bioavailability in Human Adults

Parameter	Basal Diet	
	Alone	+Ca
Study 1: (with 200 mg ascorbic acid)		(Ca phosphate)
# Subjects	8	8
Mn intake, mg/day	2.82	2.82
Fecal Mn, mg/day	1.55[b]	2.03[a]
Apparent Mn retention, mg/day	+1.27[a]	+0.79[b]
% Mn retention	45.04[a]	28.01[b]
Study 2: (with no added ascorbic acid)		(Ca lactate)
# Subjects	10	10
Mn intake, mg/day	4.03	4.03
Fecal Mn, mg/day	3.81[a]	3.57[a]
Apparent Mn retention, mg/day	+0.12[a]	+0.46[b]
% Mn retention	2.98[a]	11.41[b]

Means with different letter superscripts are significantly different at p<0.05.

Comparative effects of calcium lactate and milk on apparent manganese utilization by humans are shown on Table II (7). In this study, 10 adult human subjects were fed 900 mg calcium from milk or 916 mg of calcium from calcium lactate/subject/day. Calcium provided by the basal diet was maintained constant. The increase in fecal manganese excretion with the calcium lactate supplemented diet in comparison to values when milk was the supplemental manganese source suggests that calcium supplied by milk had a lesser adverse effect on manganese absorption than did that from calcium lactate (Table II).

Table II. Manganese Status as Affected by Milk and Calcium Lactate

Diet	Mn Intake	Mn Excretion		Mn Balance
		Urine	Feces	
	mg/day	mg/day	mg/day	mg/day
Basal diet + milk	2.40[a]	0.0210[a]	2.65[b]	-0.27[a]
Basal diet + Ca lactate	2.34[a]	0.0137[b]	3.00[a]	-0.67[b]

Means with different letter superscripts are significantly different at p<0.05.

Effects of several different, commercially-available, calcium supplements on apparent manganese utilization by humans in comparison to milk were investigated by McDermott (8). During eight randomly arranged experimental periods, 20 adult women were fed a constant, measured, laboratory controlled diet providing 400 mg of calcium/subject/day and 6.29 mg of manganese/subject/day. The high manganese content of this diet was primarily provided by whole grain ground wheat products. To this was added approximately 600 mg of calcium/subject/day from milk or from the test calcium supplement preparations. The primary objective of this project was to determine comparative effectiveness of these products relative to calcium status (2); however, measurements of parameters relative to manganese utilization were included to meet the secondary objective.

Subjects made complete collections of urine and stools throughout this study. As is true with other human studies conducted in this laboratory, feces were divided into lots representing food eaten during each experimental period by use of orally given fecal dyes and beads given at the beginning and end of each experimental period. Urine was processed into period lots on the basis of time.

Fecal manganese losses while subjects received the different calcium supplements are given in Table III. Because two of the subjects (both American/Black by nationality/race classification) were found to be lactose intolerant, data for these two individuals were omitted in calculations of mean figures. Fecal manganese losses were lowest suggesting best manganese absorption when milk was used as the calcium supplement. Greatest fecal losses of manganese occurred when the various forms of calcium carbonate were given (calcium carbonate, dolomite and oyster shell calcium).

It is reasonable to suppose that milk had a lesser effect in raising upper gastrointestinal tract pH than did the calcium

Table III. Effect of Different Calcium (Ca) Supplements on Manganese (Mn) Utilization of Humans[1]

Parameter	Milk	Oyster Shell[2]	Dolomite[3]	Ca Carbonate[4]	Ca Gluconate[5]	Ca Lactate[6]	Multi Ca Supplement[7]
Basal diet Ca, mg/day	637	637	637	637	637	637	637
Supplement Ca, mg/day	592	500	520	500	500	505	500
Basal diet Mn, mg/day	6.2 ±1.4	6.3 ±1.2	6.4 ±1.0	6.4 ±1.0	6.0 ±3.6	6.4 ±3.3	6.3 ±4.3
Fecal Mn loss, mg/day	5.33^{bc} ±2.35	6.27^{ab} ±2.20	6.60^{a} ±2.70	6.97^{a} ±3.84	5.60^{b} ±5.21	6.01^{ab} ±4.28	5.99^{ab} ±3.67
Urinary Mn loss, mg/day	0.116^{a} ±0.046	0.119^{a} ±0.032	0.126^{a} ±0.031	0.210^{a} ±0.024	0.082^{a} ±0.046	0.104^{a} ±0.050	0.112^{a} ±0.060
Mn balance, mg/day	$+0.75^{ab}$ ±2.7	-0.09^{bc} ±2.5	-0.33^{bc} ±1.5	-0.78^{c} ±1.8	$+0.32^{b}$ ±3.0	$+0.29^{b}$ ±2.8	$+0.20^{b}$ ±4.7

[1] Recalculated from McDermott (8).

[2] Oyster shell calcium with vitamin D, 2 tablets supplied 500 mg calcium. Oyster shell powder and vitamin D, Walgreens Laboratories, Inc., Chicago, IL 60632.

[3] Dolomite calcium, 4 tablets supplied 520 mg calcium carbonate and 320 mg magnesium as magnesium carbonate. Nutri-Plus Nutritional Products, Los Angeles, CA 91331.

[4] Bio Cal Calcium, 1 tablet supplied 500 mg calcium as calcium carbonate. Miles Laboratories, Inc., Elkhart, IN 46515.

[5] Mega Cal calcium with vitamin D, 1 tablet supplied 500 mg calcium and 100 mg vitamin D, derived from egg shells, oyster shells, calcium lactate, calcium gluconate, calcium carbonate, non-fat dried milk, malted milk and dairy sweet whey. Holistic Products Corp., East Rutherford, NJ 07073.

[6] Calcium gluconate, 8 tablets supplied 500 mg calcium, Pioneer Specialty Foods, Fargo, ND 58102.

[7] Calcium lactate, 6 tablets supplied 505 mg calcium, General Nutrition Corp., Pittsburgh, PA 15222.

carbonate supplements. As previously discussed, an increase in gastrointestinal tract pH would be expected to inhibit the absorption of manganese by oxidizing it from its absorbable +2 valence state to the +3 or +4 valence state. Milk diets were once customarily used in the treatment of peptic ulcers. This practice was rationalized on the basis that calcium in the milk would neutralize the excess gastric acid (9-12). However, current research suggests that the protein in milk actually stimulates gastric acid secretion. Hence, unlike the other calcium supplements, milk might enhance rather than inhibit manganese absorption.

The possible adverse effect of calcium on manganese utilization may be viewed in either the positive or the negative sense since manganese is a toxic agent when consumed in excessive amounts. Hard water is characterized by its high content of calcium and magnesium in comparison to soft water. Absorption of the manganese isotope ^{54}Mn was found to be reduced significantly from a solution containing calcium chloride in comparison to its absorption from deionized water (13). In a second experiment, absorption of ^{54}Mn was significantly enhanced in mice by chronic deprivation of a combination of calcium and magnesium or by calcium deprivation alone but not by a deprivation of magnesium alone in comparison to ^{54}Mn absorption in control mice. The authors concluded that water hardness may protect against absorption of potentially toxic amounts of manganese. Conversely, it could be concluded that the apparent adverse effect of water hardness on manganese absorption could elicit manganese deficiency under conditions of low manganese intakes.

In conclusion, research results indicate that calcium apparently inhibits the absorption of manganese from the intestinal tract. Different sources of calcium apparently affect manganese to varying degrees. Whether or not this is due to changes in intestinal acidity/alkalinity, to possible competition between manganese and calcium for absorption sites, or to a combination of factors is unknown.

Acknowledgments

Published as Nebraska Agricultural Research Division Paper No. 8425. Supported by Nebraska Agricultural Division Project 91-031 and USDA, CSRS Project W-143.

Literature Cited

1. Adrians, D.C. Trace Elements in the Terrestrial Environment; Springer-Vertag: New York, 1986; p. 263-297.
2. Kohls, K.; Kies, C.; and Fox, H.M. Fed. Proc. 1986, 45(3), 374 (Abstract #1277).
3. Miller, R.C.; Keith, T.B.; McCarty, M.A. and Thorp, W.T.S. Proc. Soc. Expt. Biol. Med. 1940, 45, 50.
4. Wilgus, H.S. and Dalton, A.R. J. Nutr. 1939, 18, 35.
5. Hawkins, C.E.; Wise, G.H.; Matrone, G.; and Waugh, R.H. J. Dairy Sci. 1955, 38, 536.
6. Kowalski, C.F. M.S. Thesis, University of Nebraska-Lincoln, 1983.

7. Vigneau, L.E.   M.S. Thesis, University of Nebraska-Lincoln, 1986.
8. McDermott, S.D.   M.S. Thesis, University of Nebraska-Lincoln, 1986.
9. Lennar-Hones, J.E. and Barbouris, N.   Gut 1965, 6, 113.
10. Ingelfinger, F.J.   In Controversy in Internal Medicine; Ingelfinger, F.J.; Relman, A.S. and Finland, M., Eds.; W.B. Saunders: Philadelphia, 1966.
11. Peterson, W.L.; Sturdevant, R.A.L.; and Frankl, H.D.   N. Engl. J. Med. 1977, 297, 341.
12. Zeman, F.J.   Clinical Nutrition and Dietetics; Collamore Press: Lexington, MA; p. 139.
13. VanBurneveld, A.A. and VandenHamer, C.J.A.   Nutr. Res. 1985, (Suppl 1), 345.

RECEIVED May 12, 1987

Author Index

Affiliation Index

Subject Index

Production by Paula M. Bérard
Indexing by Colleen P. Stamm
Jacket design by Carla L. Clemens

Elements typeset by Hot Type Ltd., Washington, DC
Printed and bound by Maple Press Co., York, PA

Related Books

Nutritional Bioavailability of Calcium
Edited by Constance Kies
200 pp; clothbound; ISBN 0–8412–0907–3

Nutritional Bioavailability of Zinc
Edited by George E. Inglett
279 pp; clothbound; ISBN 0–8412–0760–7

Nutritional Bioavailability of Iron
Edited by Constance Kies
204 pp; clothbound; ISBN 0–8412–0746–1

Recent Books

Personal Computers for Scientists: A Byte at a Time
By Glenn I. Ouchi
276 pp; clothbound; ISBN 0–8412–1000–4

The ACS Style Guide: A Manual for Authors and Editors
Edited by Janet S. Dodd
264 pp; clothbound; ISBN 0–8412–0917–0

Silent Spring Revisited
Edited by Gino J. Marco, Robert M. Hollingworth, and William Durham
214 pp; clothbound; ISBN 0–8412–0980–4

Chemical Demonstrations: A Sourcebook for Teachers
By Lee R. Summerlin and James L. Ealy, Jr.
192 pp; spiral bound; ISBN 0–8412–0923–5

Phosphorus Chemistry in Everyday Living, Second Edition
By Arthur D. F. Toy and Edward N. Walsh
362 pp; clothbound; ISBN 0–8412–1002–0

Pharmacokinetics: Processes and Mathematics
By Peter G. Welling
ACS Monograph 185; 290 pp; ISBN 0–8412–0967–7

Liquid Membranes: Theory and Applications
Edited by Richard D. Noble and J. Douglas Way
ACS Symposium Series 347; 196 pp; ISBN 0–8412–1407–7

For further information and a free catalog of ACS books, contact:
American Chemical Society
Distribution Office, Department 225
1155 16th Street, NW, Washington, DC 20036
Telephone 800-227-5558